MAKE ME YOUR DWELLING PLACE

(Recovering from Loss)

A Novel by T. L. Best

Published by
T. L. Best

Contact Author T. L. Best

tlbest@outlook.com

Instagram: @ tajuanagooding

Book Designed by Geiszel Godoy

Table of Contents

Dedication

This book is dedicated to my amazing children. We endured together and came out victorious. I love you to life!

Chapter 1

The Dream

"Jake, close the other door!" I yell to my husband, frantically. I hear the sounds of the wolves as they come closer and closer. I panic, my breathing labored and loud. My daughter and I hold one door closed while my husband, Jake, holds the other.

Wind swirls around us, pushing the doors open as we scramble to keep them all closed.

There is a third door. We don't see it. Strangely, I know it's there, but I can't get to it. It's behind a wall and no amount of effort will allow me to reach it. There is an outside presence, something forcing its way inside. My house is unprotected and that outside force is trying to break in. Fear holds me like a vice. The three of us try desperately, using every ounce of strength we have, to keep the door closed.

I think, "what are we going to do?" Jake can't get to the third door, he doesn't know it's there. Hail suddenly crashes through the ceiling, falling like small, snowy bombs all around us. The wind breaks through the walls, swirling around us like the uncontrollable force that it is. And the wolves still grow closer. I feel their presence, can almost hear their breathing. My heart races. The barking grows louder and the sheer volume of creatures outside grows increasingly obvious. There are a lot of them.

They are going to storm into our house any minute.

———————————

My eyes opened. The details of the dream settled over my mind like a haze. It took me longer to wake up than normal. I had to get ready for work, had to get my children ready for school. But as I got dressed, I couldn't help but dwell on the question, "what just happened?" Normally when I dream like this it means something substantial. I couldn't help but feel the weight of its relevance. I knew it meant something. I just didn't know what.

"Jenna," I asked my daughter, "do you have your homework?" I snapped back into reality. I needed to make sure that the children were fully prepared for their day.

"Oh, I almost forgot," she responded. I constantly must remind her about things. And in my dream-haze, this was hard.

As I continued to get my children ready, I thought about my dream. It was almost as if I was still there. I knew I needed to seek help with its meaning, and I knew just who to ask.

The moment I arrived at work I called my mentor, Sister Keller. Sister Keller is a long time friend who relocated to California with her husband about three years ago. She is a counselor, prayer warrior, minister, and someone I can trust. She has counseled me for many years, through many things, and has never been wrong. Also, she is very good at interpreting dreams. This is what I now needed her for most. Her wisdom, to me, was invaluable.

On my way to work, the dream continued to swirl through my thoughts, never increasing in clarity. I was three months pregnant with our third child. I sat and imagined the baby sitting in my belly, barely there but continuously present. I counted the minutes on the clock, watching the hands gradually tick closer to what I considered to be their destination: The moment in which I would talk with Sister Keller. She, I knew, would have the answers.

Finally, I called her. She was going to give reason to the night that I had, to the strange, life-like sensations that brushed my psyche. For the most part, people don't think of dreams as having any real relevance Sister's job. Most people would blame it on something they ate the night before or an overactive mind. With Sister Keller though, she simply knew that

God communicated with his people through dreams. She was always there to interpret the dream for me.

I called her from work. While I had been nervous in anticipation of our conversation, the moment she picked up the phone, I wasn't. We first exchanged niceties, talking about the kids and our morning routines. Then I really began to speak, began to describe the dream in the vivid detail in which it had come to me.

I started off by telling her about how Jake, Jenna, and I were in this room, about how I wasn't sure where we were exactly, but I did know that the room was white. We were standing in the middle of the floor and wind was swirling all around us. Hail was falling from the ceiling. I could hear wolves barking and running towards the house, but I couldn't see them. I could only hear them. We raced towards the two doors, trying to close them in order to keep the wolves out. But when I stepped forward to close my door, I saw another door to my left that was hidden. The wind was so strong that it took both Jenna and I to keep the door closed. Jake closed his door. I yell to Jake to close the third door, but he can't. The dream finishes as the wolves continue to grow closer and the third door is still left open.

I was nervous as I told her about the dream, trying to get it out even as I couldn't breathe. Telling her about this dream seemed to use all the air that I had.

Finally, I paused. "So, Sister Keller," I finally asked nervously, "what do you think it means?"

She paused, there was a moment of silence on the line. But I knew that she was sure when she said, "there is a challenge coming against your family."

I sighed. I didn't say much, because even though I needed Sister Keller to confirm it for me, I had already known that what she said was true. My family was about to face a challenge indeed.

The Challenge

The night we conceived Isaac, Jake told me our relationship was the best it had ever been. I found this hard to believe. Our relationship, in my opinion, needed a lot of work. There were issues that weren't being addressed. However, at the time, I believed what I wanted to believe. Our relationship was great, I thought, despite the evidence to the contrary. I simply wanted us to be okay. So, when he said that we were okay, I believed him. And because I believed that he meant what he said, we conceived Isaac that night.

I knew I was pregnant almost immediately. Everything was in alignment to make this happen. The birth control had failed, and it was right at that time of month when conception was most probable. I made an appointment with the doctor and, sure enough, there was a tiny dot on the screen. While it was too early to detect a heartbeat, I came back in two weeks for another ultrasound.

Sure enough, there was a heartbeat on the screen, beating strong and full. I was definitely pregnant.

We were excited. The timing wasn't great. Our second child was only a year and a half old and getting pregnant so soon wasn't really the plan. But our third child was on its way, soon to be fully formed. Nine months may seem like a long time, but it isn't. We began house hunting right away. This was exciting. We could visualize the way our lives would soon look. Our family would be a little more complete. We could envision our children's rooms, the new baby's nursery.

But house hunting is also daunting. Houses are expensive, especially in New York. None of the houses that we liked were in our budget. There was one house that we loved. It was in Cambria Heights and it was beautiful. It had a master bedroom on the first floor, two bedrooms on the second floor, and a nice-sized basement. None of this comes cheap though. It was costly and, unfortunately, we just couldn't afford it. Of course, none of the other houses fit our expectations.

Some nerve we had. Champagne taste with a beer wallet.

Even though house hunting was daunting, even though it was very difficult to find a place that fit our expectations, looking at the places was fun. We felt like a family, and at that point, I really did believe Jake when he said that our relationship was the best that it had ever been.

A short time later, this changed. We were sitting in our bedroom one night, the events of my day playing through my head, when Jake turned and told me that he had a question to ask.

"Ok," I responded simply.

This wasn't a normal question, but rather a question about somebody I really did not like. He told me a story about a woman named Susan and her husband. Although I don't know it at the time, Susan was the other woman. Or maybe I did know it. I did know that she was a good childhood friend of my ex-husband's. The man who was my then husband. I also knew that they had been groomed as children to one day marry each other. Once they were adults, they dated briefly. But it didn't last.

Somehow, they reconnected. I didn't know the details of this reconnect, why or how it occurred. I never told my husband that he could not have female friends. Admittedly though, I was concerned about this one. I never wanted to be the jealous type, and truthfully, I didn't think I was being jealous. I felt that my feelings were rational. The entire relationship made me uncomfortable. But discomfort is a feeling one grows to live with. And for the sake of avoiding an argument, I left the topic alone. I had learned to do this over the years. To stifle my discomfort for the sake of his. He said any suspicion towards him was disrespectful.

So that night, I sat in bed and listened to my husband tell me a story about a person I never wanted to hear about again. He told me about how her husband went to a nude bar and had a lap dance. Now, she wants to leave him. After telling me the story he paused and asked, "What should I tell her? She's asking me for counseling."

Asking my husband for counseling was not necessarily abnormal. He was a minister, so this was typical. What was not typical was how they felt about each other. Even then, I knew that there was some level of attraction. It was because of this that asking him such a question was inappropriate. I was frustrated. But beyond that, I didn't think that it was appropriate for a man who didn't even have his own marriage together to offer marital advice to someone. I know he said our relationship was fine, but throughout this anecdote, I knew that it wasn't true.

So, I said to him, calmly and without hesitation, "I don't think that you are in a place to offer counseling when you don't have your own marriage together."

I didn't hold back, and I definitely did not filter my thoughts. Jake knew how I felt and the look on his face told me he felt it. I did offer advice though. I told him that Susan should go to counseling and that she should take her husband with her. If they're willing to work on their marriage, I thought, then maybe she would leave mine alone.

Little did I know that this was the beginning of something much larger. It was only the introduction to Jake's great escape. Really, he was already gone.

A few weeks after the discussion, when I was four months pregnant, it started hailing. We were all sitting in the living room. I couldn't help but go back to that dream. It was still haunting me. Jenna, Jake, and I went outside to investigate. I couldn't believe what I was seeing. The hail was pounding down incessantly, making so much noise. I picked up a piece of hail and it was the size of a nickel, just like in the dream. I said to myself, "Lord, what are you showing me?" Even I knew at the time that this huge chunk of hail symbolized what more was to come. What more was to rain down upon our family.

My Trip to North Carolina:

It was two weeks after the hail storm, and Jake was mad at me. This was the first time, in thirteen years of marriage, that we stayed upset with each other for more than a day. Like every couple, we had our arguments. But we always resolved them quickly. This time however, I knew there was something more because Jake simply could not put the argument aside.

The reason that he was so upset was very miniscule. I had merely suggested that he work my job while I was on maternity leave. My job, like his, was very low impact. He worked nights, so I thought it was a good idea. This way, we could keep two pay checks coming in. These two pay checks were invaluable to us, and I couldn't rest well knowing that, even if for a limited time, we would be down to only one. I thought that this would have been a logical choice, but for Jake it wasn't. While I was thinking about how we were going to feed our family, Jake was thinking about something (or someone) else entirely.

17

Jake was excessively irate. With the way he acted, an outsider would have thought that I had asked him to do something far worse. At the time, I couldn't figure out why this made him so mad. I eventually realized that he wasn't mad about that at all.

I believe now though that his anger was a scheme, a way to justify leaving. He needed a reason. He couldn't simply say that he was leaving his pregnant wife because he felt like it, so he had to create a drama surrounding my suggestion that he briefly work two jobs. I now know that if a person wants to leave their spouse, they will find an excuse to do it. The reasons don't have make to sense, they just must exist.

Abandoned spouses spend hours of their days and days of their years trying to make sense of a situation that simply has no logic. We may never know why our spouses left us. Sometimes, people are dissatisfied with their relationships for any number of reasons. People get bored, or restless, or they change, or they simply see one moment of monotony or instability as an indicator that their relationship is not everything that it should be. Relationships rarely are. They're work. Kids come along and parents need to earn money. Time together is short. We work hard and we grow tired but at the end of the day that relationship is supposed to be our rock, our haven.

Unfortunately, that doesn't always work. People look outside of their marriages, rather than within them, to fix them. They don't look at the situation as repairable, but rather as a reason to seek escape. No spouse is perfect. None of us are the perfect wives, or the perfect husbands, but we are *the* spouse. No amount of dissatisfaction makes it okay for somebody to cheat, for someone to look for escape in such an emotionally harmful way. This is unacceptable, always.

Two weeks later, Jake was still mad at me. This level of anger was rarely present within our marriage up to this point, especially for something as totally trivial as me trying to secure our future finances. I simply could not comprehend his degree of emotion.

He said that I didn't care about him. "When am I supposed to rest," he asked me. My idea was simply a suggestion, a way to begin brainstorming ways to safeguard against future financial issues. Going from two to one paycheck would be a challenge. I wanted us to talk about it now, while we had time. I was carrying his child and would soon give birth to him. I couldn't comprehend his anger. But that's because, emotionally, he was no longer my spouse. He was a stranger. My idea was meant to start a discussion. Not to end one.

I had planned a trip to visit my father towards the end of July. Still pregnant, I planned the entire trip to North Carolina. And, I drove the entire way. I had my two girls and my niece with me. Jake came along too, even though he was still upset. Despite his anger, he still wanted to go on the trip with me. He didn't, however, want to help with any of the planning or execution of the trip. He wanted to sit next to me and seethe, to make his anger known. So together, we set out for North Carolina. While everything was somewhat okay on the way down, everything escalated once we arrived.

This was a special trip for me because I was operating as an emissary on behalf of my sisters and I, to check up on my father. He had a tendency to miss his doctor's appointments, and these appointments were important for his health. He was a stubborn man, and it was my job to drive down and get him to the doctor. Needless to say, my visit had a purpose. Although in better circumstances I would have appreciated the support of my husband, he was not offering anything of the sort. And I could not help but wonder why he would make the trip with me in his state of irritation. It made no sense.

My plan was to spend a week at my father's house because I wanted to stay and celebrate his birthday. During the course of this week, tension only escalated. It started when, one night, I woke up around 2am to hear Jake speaking on the phone with a friend. He was talking to his friend, in a derogatory manner, about an event that had happened over two years prior. Because of the time lapse, I simply could not buy his animosity towards the event. I was hurt when I heard the statements that he made, especially when I considered the fact that he had looked me in the eye and told me that our relationship was okay while complaining about it to someone else. I also couldn't believe that he had the nerve to talk about me like that in my own father's house.

An event such as this one, that is lacking in any basic respect or consideration, can only be the beginning of the end. It only got worse from there. A few days later, still at my father's house, Jake's phone began to ring. Instinctively, I picked it up to bring to him. I would consider this typical. I generally tried to respect Jake's privacy. This was not a way to spy, but rather a very typical gesture within a married couple's life. I wanted to bring my husband his phone because it was ringing, and he was not there to get it.

But when I picked it up, I saw that he had been texting Susan.

"Are you okay?" his message read.

While this alone would not have been alarming, her response made the exchange troublesome.

"I am ok, babe," she replied.

Friends rarely, if ever, call one another babe. I know this. Everyone knows this. So, I confronted him.

"She calls you babe now?" I asked Jake, angry.

"Why are you looking through my phone?" was his immediate response.

"I wasn't looking through your phone?" I responded, frustrated. "Your phone rang, and I was bringing it to you."

Of course, this answer didn't appease him and, even though I saw the inappropriate exchange, he was the one who felt the entitlement to tell me that I was in the wrong. This event was the tipping point, the means through which he could tell me that he was leaving. He had the nerve to tell me that it was what I wanted, even though he and I both knew that it wasn't. I wanted what was best for my children, wanted stability for them, wanted the presence of their father. We had worked so hard, as a couple, to find our daughter some element of stability in school. I simply could not understand the lack of care, the complete dissociation it would take, to stir her world like that, why he wouldn't mind upsetting her. We had only recently been house hunting. We had created the stable foundations upon which a family is built; however, I could feel that it was all about to come crashing down.

The implications of his actions were obvious to me. Maybe they weren't to him, or maybe he just didn't care about any implications beyond the immediate. Thinking of my children, I began to weep. Right there, where I stood in that bedroom, I mourned for them. There was a strong possibility that they would grow up without a father.

At that point, my husband was like an addict. He was an addict, and like most addicts, he didn't even know it. I could call him out, confront him, and his behavior would only grow more obvious. After the blow up over the phone, rather than assessing his actions and considering their impact, he continued to call her. I was forced to watch him do this, to live with the knowledge of these calls, while we were still in my father's house.

"What's wrong with you?" I would think, as I watched him tear our family apart. One evening, I sat and saw him get aroused, and I knew the stimulation was coming from someone who was not me. At this point, what was once suspicion was now growing increasingly obvious. I was consistently sad, always upset. Ms. Bethel, my stepmom, told me to calm down because I was pregnant. She was right, I needed to consider the baby, but who has the emotional control to respond positively to a situation like that? I felt like a prisoner in my own body. I wanted to burst, but I was afraid that an outburst like this would hurt my baby. I couldn't react the way I wanted to, couldn't scream like I wanted to. I needed to throw my emotions into the air, and I couldn't.

As planned, we stayed for about a week before returning home. My father tried to reassure me, tried to tell me that it might not be what I thought it was. Maybe there was an alternative explanation, he tried to tell me. But I knew what was going on because the Lord had showed me in a dream a few nights before.

In the dream, words were flowing out of my husband's ears and through a large, industrial sized printer. This dream, like the dream I had about the hail, was vivid and lasting. I knew that it meant something and, after thinking about it, I knew what it was that the Lord was trying to show me. My dream had meant something before. I knew that this one did too. I interpreted this dream as something telling me that the proof, I needed to confirm that my husband was having an affair was in print. In other words, it was written down somewhere. It was as though the Lord was telling me to be patient. I will bring you the proof you need, he seemed to say to me.

But like any woman in my position, I did not want to wait to move forward. I wanted the Holy Spirit to lead me, but I didn't want to wait. So, I became my own guide and searched through everything. I looked at his cell phones, his emails. I was relentless. I was determined to find the proof that I needed. I couldn't live with that lingering trace of doubt, with the nagging knowledge that I knew but could not prove that my husband was seeing somebody else. In my search, I discovered my husband's attachment to porn. I was shocked. We were ministers at church. We must live our lives to a certain set of moral standards, and it seemed that his were slipping. I never would have expected this from him. But of course, there was a lot of behavior I would not have expected from him. If I was learning anything, it was that I needed to expect what was to be unexpected. To know that my life and my expectations could change at any moment.

Even though the evidence was fast accumulating, I continued to search. And in my continued search I saw a text that he had sent her saying, "good morning sunshine." I was furious. This text was not a text between friends, no matter if I told myself that or not. Good morning Sunshine. This insisted on some level of intimacy, something beyond friendship. This made me furious. I approached him. I insisted on transparency and honesty in my relationships, and this was clearly not something with which he was providing me. I wanted an explanation. Maybe I wanted him to convince me that it wasn't what I thought it was, but I think that what I wanted was just one clear answer in this mess of confusion and fury.

Instead, he scolded me for going through his phone. I just couldn't understand why I was being scolded. I felt like the mistress, not the wife. He didn't feel guilt, but he tried his best to make me feel guilty for wanting to be heard, for wanting the answers I felt like I was entitled to. And because I clearly was not getting the answers from him, I sought them somewhere else. I called Pastor Matt.

Pastor Matt was a longtime friend of our family's. I thought that he could help me because he knew us both, knew us through our relationship. He would have our family's interest in mind. Maybe he could help me, and maybe he could help my husband understand what he was doing. So, one morning, on my way to work, I called Pastor Matt and I explained the situation to him. I started telling him about my husband's behavior and my fears for my family. His immediate response was, "I told him to stop calling that girl."

I was shocked. I sat, stunned in silence. He knew about the situation, and the reason he knew about it was because my husband had been telling different people about this young lady and his plans on leaving his family. This was something that my husband was so confident about that he felt fine telling other people what he was doing. He did not feel like he owed his wife any answers, but he had talked to others. I was in utter amazement, plainly disgusted by his complete lack of concern. I felt horrible.

Nevertheless, I wanted to save my marriage. I wanted to salvage my family, to keep my children's father in their lives. I still thought that Pastor Matt could help. He and I devised a plan to try and bring my husband back. He advised me to avert my husband's attention away from the other woman and back towards me by increasing my womanly wiles and seducing my husband.

As per his advice, I set out to try and rekindle the spark that had died. I went shopping at a Macy's department store and bought lingerie. I prepared special meals and scheduled date nights. We would sit and eat and play games of chess. I thought that bouts of undivided attention would strengthen our bond, remind us both why we fell in love in the first place. But despite my attempts, his attention was still concentrated elsewhere. Even when we had sex, he wasn't thinking of me. l looked into his eyes and I could see that he was thinking of her. I was a body in front of him, while she was the one situated in his mind. The rejection was too much for me. I had tried to again seduce him, had tried to dedicate more time and energy to him, and he still could not appreciate the effort. He said that his feelings for me were just cut off. At this point, I knew that he didn't want to try and make this relationship work. He had already made up his mind.

The pain that I felt was unbearable. One day, at work, I stood in the conference room wailing. I had called Pastor Matt, screaming to him about how my husband no longer loved me, no longer wanted me. I never planned my life this way. I was a virgin when I married. I waited six years to have my first child in order to become financially stable, and I had planned for my children to grow up in a two-parent household. I had done everything right, had done everything that I was supposed to do. And despite this, I felt like I was being punished. My husband had no regard for the life we had built together. In only the span of a few months, all the plans we once made were destroyed.

The Trip to Florida

It was August and I was six months pregnant. Jake and I were sitting in our bedroom. He was at the foot of the bed, and I was at the head, when he turned around to look at me and said that he wanted to take a trip to Florida for his birthday. Immediately, I responded in a high-pitched voice, "you are going to Florida to visit your girlfriend?

I knew that's what he was going to do. No defense that he could provide would convince me otherwise, but still, he responded, "No, I am going to visit my friend Steve." He was a liar. I could not comprehend why he continued to lie when he knew that I knew the truth. And this lie was so blatant, so infuriating in how obvious it was. He and the girlfriend shared the same birthday. I was sure that he was going to Florida so that they could celebrate together. I can't explain how difficult this was for me. I was pregnant, with two kids, and he wanted to take a trip to Florida to visit his girlfriend. Rather than celebrate his birthday with his family, he wanted to spend it with the very person who was going to destroy us. I was insane with anger. A heated argument ensued. I don't remember all of the content of the argument, but I do remember that despite my frustration, he went to Florida a week after his birthday. The trip had been planned whether I supported it or not.

His behavior grew increasingly bizarre as the trip to Florida loomed closer. Even though I never asked him to, never even suggested it, he started sleeping on the couch. I think he needed to detach himself from me before he could fully enjoy his rendezvous. Not out of any loyalty towards me, of course, but out of a distorted loyalty towards her. He didn't want to cheat on his mistress with his wife. I thought of this insanity as almost a joke. If I didn't maintain a dark sense of humor about all of it, I knew that I would completely crumble. It was all too depressing.

The night that he left for Florida he told me that he accidentally booked his flight to Tampa. His friend Steve lived in Miami. For any who are uncertain about how absurd this lie was, I will outline the geography of the Florida state. Tampa is on the Northern edge of Florida and Miami is at the Southern tip. The state is huge. The girl lived on the outskirts of Tampa, so this was very obviously not a coincidence. It was solidified. He was going to visit her.

Up until this point, I never wanted to call her. But with the visit looming, I needed to confront her. I had to know, for certain, why my husband was going to visit her. As he was leaving, he said for me to lose her number. Instead, I immediately picked up the phone and called the girlfriend.

"Hello," she answered. I asked her why my husband was going to visit her, outlining the knowledge that I had about his trip. I told her that I knew he was flying into Tampa, and that I knew that's where she lived. I wanted answers.

Instead, she only responded," I don't live in Tampa."

"You live right on the outskirts of Tampa," I responded, growing increasingly frustrated.

I wanted answers and nobody, not my husband, not her, would provide me with any. They provided me only with half-hearted excuses or lies that were almost comical in their degree of obviousness.

What was even more comical was that she then tried to tell me that she had always been there for Jake and me. I could not believe the audacity it took to tell me that she had been there for my family, for my children and I, while she was about to spend the weekend with my husband. If she cared about my family, if she even cared about my husband, she would not be playing a role in ripping apart our lives.

After I hung up with the girlfriend, I received a call from Jake. He was irate because I called her. "I asked you not to do that," he said. I don't know how he expected me to stay calm in a situation such as this. He wanted me to sit with the knowledge of what he was about to do while he traveled comfortably down the coast. It was unbelievable. He left me alone, pregnant and with two children. My deepest fear at that moment was that he would not return on the day he promised our oldest daughter that he would. Our youngest daughter was only two years old, and she didn't fully understand the whole situation. But our oldest was taking on the full brunt of it. I could only imagine how she felt as a seven-year-old; her whole world was spinning out of control. I had to live with his broken promises and it was destroying me, but a child of that age deserved to be spared his dishonesty. I was worried that she would soon be hit with it too.

After my phone call with Jake I called his mother. I began to scream, "Why is your son leaving me to go to Florida and visit Susan?" His mother didn't say much. She just listened to me. I could tell that she was upset, and probably even angry at her son's behavior. No mother wants to hear that the boy she raised is being a horrible man. Nobody wants to hear how their son is hurting his family.

When I hung up with her, Jake's sister called. She began to pray for me, telling me to center myself and to think of the kids. I appreciated her gesture, and it did help me to calm down a bit. But the entire time I couldn't help thinking, "how can you tell me to center myself and think of the children when that is who I am crying for?" I was hurt, certainly. But I was primarily grieving for the children. I was wailing less for me and more for them.

Jake called while he was in Florida. I told him not to disappoint our daughter by not returning when he told her he would. But I knew at this point that Jake has lost it. He wasn't reliable. He wasn't considerate. His mind was entirely focused on his own life, on his own pleasure. I no longer knew my husband. He was a totally different person. I could never guess what he would do next.

Jake returned and our daughter was happy to see him. My pastor friend said that I was good because I had not changed the locks. Although I was angry, and I would have had every right to change the locks, I was not yet ready to take steps towards shutting him out of our life. For the sake of my children, I wanted him to be there. I did not want my daughter to feel the disappointment she would feel if her father did not walk through the door. We won't discuss what happened on the trip, but it had changed Jake. He literally smelled different. He came back and he lay down next to me as if nothing happened. How he could pretend like I didn't know, how he could even consider the fact that he could do this to our family and then pretend that he didn't, was too much. I turned and said to him, "you didn't get any while you were there? What a shame for you to travel all that way and not get any."

He promptly got up and left the room.

We were estranged from one another for the remainder of my pregnancy. The time when a husband should most be there for his wife was instead a time in which I felt him drifting away. In addition, I was still trying to finish my directorship with Mary Kay Cosmetics, which was far more difficult because of the stress. I couldn't focus on anything but the challenges we were facing at home. It was too hard to focus on work when I was trying to figure out how to retain my own husband so that our family would not fall apart.

I was due at the end of November, but I gave birth a month early. I went into labor October 27, 2009. I had gone to my Mary Kay meeting and I was feeling very tired, but I had "pressed my way," as they say in church. Those past months had made me used to struggle. Physical pain and exhaustion were nothing in comparison to the emotionally draining experiences I was having at home.

I left the meeting early because I had pain in my right leg. I reached home and changed into my night clothes and was resting on the bed when I started to feel a trickle of water going down my leg. I went into the living room and told Jake that I thought my water broke. We waited a few minutes just to make sure, and then we called Pastor Matt to take me to the hospital. We loaded everyone into Pastor Matt's car and began our journey. Once we arrived at the hospital, Jake went inside with me to check-in and then left to go with Pastor Matt to drop the kids at my mother-in-law's house. Afterwards, he came back. This all started around 10 o'clock at night. The hospital decided to let me relax all night. There was no heavy labor, but they must keep you once your water breaks. The entire time, there was no real communication between Jake and me. I was giving birth to his child and he still could not manage to value me, to love me like he was supposed to. Childbirth should be a moment in which a husband is solidly there for his wife in every way. He was there, but only physically.

We knew that we were having a boy. Of course, Jake wanted him to be a junior, but I thought, considering recent events, that this would not be the right choice to make. I felt the Lord wanted me to name him something else. My son would have his own name. Early the next morning, my doctor came into the room and said that he would like to start me on Pitocin, a drug that induces contractions. I told him to wait until I had my epidural. I don't like pain. So, they called the anesthesiologist, and when all was right with the world, we proceeded.

Our son was born a few hours later, and I named him Isaac Gabriel Jacobs. I gave him Jake's middle name, Gabriel. I hoped that this would be enough for Jake, that his son have his middle name. I'm glad now that I did not give hm Jake's first name. I can't imagine calling him by the name of a person who would eventually abandon him. It would have been too painful for us both. To bestow my son with his name would have been an honor for Jake. But to receive an honor, one must be worthy.

The day after Isaac was born, he was placed in the neonatal unit because his sugar levels kept dropping.

This could be a life altering situation because it could have affected his mental capacity. The hospital tried to give Isaac a chance to regulate his sugar on his own, but that didn't work. Things were happening so quickly that the hospital staff didn't give me a chance to process the situation. I called my pediatrician, and she told me that the hospital was doing the right thing. They hurriedly moved Isaac. Every second was vital. Every minute lost would count against him and his brain functioning properly. I am now glad that the hospital acted so promptly, but in those first few moments and days with my child, I thought that they were acting without my permission. I just wanted my baby and I wanted him to be okay. I was tired of chaos in our lives.

I was also worried that the reason his blood sugar kept dropping was due to a condition I had developed while I was pregnant with him. It's called PICA. PICA is an iron deficiency, and when a person is experiencing PICA (due to stress or otherwise) they eat things such as clay, laundry detergent, starch, rocks. Non-congestible items. I started eating ice. I had a bizarre and irresistible craving for ice. I searched constantly for some that wouldn't break my teeth. I started perusing the neighborhood for ice that was easy to chew. I now know that, outside of the hospital, Dunkin Donuts has the best ice chips. I met a lady who worked across the street from where I worked. She made me a slushy every morning so that I could chew on the ice. She would put ice in a blender and add strawberry compote. It was a little too sweet, but it helped to satisfy my craving for ice, which was constant. Because of these cravings, I blamed myself for Isaac's dilemma. I thought that maybe the PICA and his low blood sugar could be connected.

They were, thankfully, able to stabilize his blood sugar. But this also meant that I could not bring him home from the hospital when I left. Leaving behind a newborn baby, especially one in a fragile condition such as his, is extremely difficult. I tried to stay an extra day, but the hospital regulations would not allow it because the insurance company wouldn't cover the expense. So, I was depressed when Pastor Matt picked me up to take me home. I wanted to be with my baby. I felt empty, sad.

On the way home, Pastor Matt asked if I needed anything first. I told him that I would like to stop at the grocery store, so we did. He joked with me about how slow I was walking. "You give birth to a seven - pound baby and see how fast you walk," I said to myself. I was grateful for Pastor Matt's help, but I was tired and emotionally exhausted.

I bought groceries and he brought me home. It was about ten at night, and Jake was there with the girls. We hadn't spoken since the hospital. I had been left to deal with Isaac's condition alone, to sit and wonder about his condition's origins, to hope that he would be okay. It was another moment, after a string of many, where I could have really used my husband's help. I walked up the stairs slowly, still very sore. Pastor Matt brought the groceries inside. Despite the tension between Jake and I, I wanted to see him and my daughters. I craved the comfort I thought that my family could provide me.

But as I walked up the stairs, Jake walked down with his backpack in tow. It took me a moment to register what was happening. I couldn't understand that my husband was leaving because I could not believe it possible that a husband would leave his wife after she had just given birth to their son. That's why, when he stood there and told me that he was leaving because I didn't name the baby after him, Pastor Matt and I only stood and looked at each other in shock.

"Are you okay?" Pastor Matt asked me, finally.

I said yes, but I didn't mean it. I had no idea what we were going to do. I was just out of the hospital and exhausted. I was not physically ready to handle the responsibility of caring for two children and a baby. And I was not emotionally prepared to care for my daily duties while also dealing with the repercussions of having an absent husband. I needed to grieve, but there was no time for this. I was now a single parent, whether I was ready for that or not.

I picked up the phone and called my father. He had mentioned that he wanted to visit after the baby was born, and because I really needed his help, I wanted to ascertain exactly when he would be there. Even though I was heartbroken, I found that I was attempting to take the action that I needed to take.

"Daddy," I said, "Jake left." I explained to my father his reasoning, telling him that he left because I did not name the baby after him.

"So that is the reason he is going to use," my father responded. We both knew that this was simply an excuse, something he felt he could use to do what he had wanted to do for a long time. I recognized it, and my father recognized it. My father said that he would call me right back and hung up.

After only a few minutes he called me back to say that he and Ms. Annie would be there in a couple of days. I was relieved that my father was coming. At least then I would not be burdened with everything on my own, immediately. I knew that I was in for a major challenge.

I never thought that I would be in this situation. I did everything I could in order to prevent this kind of thing from happening. I had avoided this kind of drama by all means necessary, and yet it somehow found me. I had married another believer. We both had the same Christian beliefs. One of which was that you don't commit adultery.

The Package

The next morning, I received a call from the hospital letting me know that I could bring Isaac home. I was so relieved. I had never before experienced leaving the hospital without my newborn, and it was a strange sensation. I had carried Isaac inside of me for nearly nine months, so understandibly giving birth to him and not being able to have him with me all the time was difficult. After bringing him home, I tried to rest as much as possible. Anyone who has experienced childbirth knows of the physical aches and pains of bringing a child into the world. They say that you are the closest to death when you are giving birth. Afterwards, you have to be very careful because you can hemorrhage. My body was slowly recovering.

By law you are supposed to take your baby for his or her first doctor's visit within one week of the birth. Isaac came home on a Saturday and I took him to the doctor on the following Wednesday. The pediatrician's primary focus for this visit was to check for jaundice (yellowing of the skin), which would indicate that something was wrong with the baby's liver. Isaac's first doctor's visit went well, and everything was fine. I was happy that everything with Isaac was going smoothly. Even though Jake had left, and I was reeling from shock, I was still a mother. My first concern was my baby's health.

Once I left the doctor's office, I stopped at the corner store for a few things, and as I was driving home, I looked back and thought, "I am the mother to three children." I remember looking back and seeing three small heads in the backseat of my car and wondering, "how did this happen?" I was genuinely amazed. These three children meant everything to me.

This consumed my thoughts as I drove home and parked on the side of my house. I walked to the front door and was greeted by the mailman, who handed me a package and asked me to sign for it. I accepted the package and finished bringing the kids inside, along with the groceries. The entire time I was curious as to the package's contents. I had no idea what could be inside. It wasn't a box, but an envelope, so I figured that it must be a document of some kind. After I settled the children, I sat down at my dining room table and ripped the package open. I was nervous, curious. What could it be?

I looked at the first page and saw that it said, "your husband and my wife are having an illicit affair." Selah means "let's think of that" in the bible. Let's think of that, I thought. I had had a dream about information getting delivered to me in word form, and here it was. Selah.

The next several pages were copies of telephone records. It cataloged the numerous times that my husband called her in one day. I would say it was about ten times a day. The sheer volume of calls that he placed was alarming. While I was worried about how we would tend to our children on one paycheck, he was calling his mistress. Constantly. The last few pages were a printout of a conversation that they had via yahoo messaging, and there seemed to be video footage involved. I knew what this implied, but I didn't want to think about it. Throughout the conversation, they talked about him coming to visit her, and they said that they would have their time together again. The conversation took place in August, and I was receiving this package in November. It looked like he probably went to see her when she lived in Delaware before relocating to Florida. The affair had been going on for a while.

I couldn't believe that I held the evidence in my hand, that it was all right there in front of me. The content of the document was difficult to read. I did not like seeing the conversations that my husband had with the other woman, the extent to which this affair had been going on. But the Lord had said that he would bring the evidence to me and bring the evidence to me he did. It could not get more concrete than that.

Although we weren't living together at the time, Jake found out that I had this information. I must have told him I had it. He followed me around the supermarket one day, telling me that the entire package was a joke. He had already left, had already made his intentions clear, and yet he still felt the need to lie to me. He made up an elaborate story of how he was trying to help Susan leave her husband, so they left the information on her home computer for him to see. It was all absurd. None of this was true, none of it could have been true. Jake was reaching, scrambling for an excuse. And the only one he could think of was bizarre and comical, in no way believable. His lies grew increasingly ridiculous with each passing day.

My mother-in-law asked me why I wouldn't allow Jake to move back in. I told her about the package, assuming that this would settle the matter. He had been cheating on me, and there was now no point in denying it. Still, she thought it was wrong of Susan's husband to send me the information. "How could he do that when you just had a baby?" She asked. I know that Jake is her son, but I couldn't believe that she was pointing the finger of blame at Susan's husband when Jake was the one who had tortured me throughout my pregnancy with his absolute disregard for me or for his family. At least the package told me the truth, which is more than I could say for Jake. Susan's husband did me a favor. Jake had tried to convince me that he didn't go and see Susan in Florida, but the package proved that he had. I had spent months and months trying to discern the real from the fake, the lies my husband told from the man that I once knew. The package was, literally, a godsend.

Susan's husband had also sent the package to her side of the family. He wanted the truth to be known. This poor man hoped that if his wife's infidelity was made more public, that his marriage could be saved. He wanted someone to convince her of her irrationality, to make her see sense. He sent me the package because he thought that, perhaps, I could convince my husband not to visit her in Florida. He was afraid of what this visit would mean, of what would happen. I couldn't bring myself to tell him that my husband had already made the trip to Florida back in September. I spoke to the husband over the phone. He intimated to me that Susan had been behaving the same way that Jake was. They could be home having a great family time and she would receive a call and leave the room and return a different person. It was as if they were possessed. Neither of them was the same people they once were. Susan's husband and I felt the same loss.

At this point, I still wanted to save my marriage. Jake was the father of my three children, and I did believe that people could make a mistake. Maybe Jake lost control, but that didn't mean that he couldn't once again regain it. If he was again put on the right path, then maybe he would see his errors and return to the person he once was. To try and save the marriage, we went to our pastor the December after the baby was born. He had a session with us, attempted to council us back together. It was ineffective though, because Jake only said that it was useless. If there is no will, then anything will be useless. Although I was frustrated, the pastor told me not to say anything. He would talk to Jake, he told me. Although I had hope that the pastor's words could in some way sway him, it didn't help.

My father stayed with me for about a month, and Jake's behavior seemed stable. However, that changed. My sister told me that once Daddy leaves, Jake would show his true self. Sure enough, he did. Once my father went back home, Jake got physical. He allowed himself to lose control to such an extent that he would harm a woman. Not just any woman, but the woman who was his wife and the mother of his three children. Although we weren't living together, he had rented a room only a few blocks away and came by quite frequently.

The incident occurred one day when we started arguing. He began to leave, avoiding any meaningful discussion as he had formed the habit of doing. I was frustrated by his incessant inability to engage in a meaningful discussion and I said "fine, leave then." I meant it. If he was going to treat me poorly, he could leave my house. But he was so angered by my statement that he picked up the child safety gate and threw it across the room towards the television. His outburst terrified me, and I knew I needed help. I grabbed the phone to try and call someone. I was holding Isaac when he violently grabbed the phone from my hand and pulled me into the master bedroom.

He was absolutely crazed, and his eyes showed it. I was terrified. "Stop looking at me like you're afraid of me," he said. But I was afraid of him. This was a side I had never before seen. Despite the infidelity and the lies, he had never before gotten so violent. I looked at him and could only think that it appeared as though something had broken inside, that something snapped that allowed him to act this way. I wondered where he had been, what he had done, what sort of event could prompt a man to act this way. He was staying with his brother; however, I didn't know if the brother was to blame for the way Jake was acting. The truth was, I had no idea who Jake was anymore. The Jake I once knew would not have done this, but the Jake I once knew also would not have cheated on his wife.

Finally, Jake calmed down and left the house. I was so relieved. He could have very seriously hurt me or the baby, he could have killed one of us. I could not predict what a man so crazed could do. Fortunately, the Lord was on our side and he would not let it be so. We were safe for the time being. At first, I wondered if I should even let him come back to the apartment. But for some reason, probably because of our history and because I could not stop thinking about our children, I still wanted to work on the marriage. I fervently hoped that with help, Jake would return to the man he once was. I asked a Pastor Matt to counsel us.

At this point, I was reaching the end of my maternity leave. I had only a few weeks left until it was time for me to return. Because I had not been working, money was tight. I had been left to pay all of the bills in Jake's absence. I would have returned to work early, but because my supervisor had hired a temporary replacement, I was prohibited from asking.

Once I was back at work though, I had to pay someone to watch the baby at home. Because my first paycheck was not a full one, I had to give the entirety of it to the sitter. I had absolutely no food in my refrigerator, but God is good, and the sitter took me food shopping, so I was able to feed my children. Although I was embarrassed, my children needed to eat. This was only one small start to what would be a very lengthy time filled with trial after trial, challenge after challenge.

Jake and I were still living separately, but after a few months we decided to try and reconcile again. This time my present pastor devised a plan of action that would hopefully bring us to some resolution in about three months. We each met separately with my pastor and then together. We drew up a contract and we had a little ceremony at our house to affirm our agreement to work the plan that the pastor had devised. For thirty days we consciously made an effort to work on our marriage. Everything was good. I was filled with hope that our marriage would work out, that we would be back to normal and that we could raise our children together under one roof.

The end of our thirty days came, and I asked Jake if he wanted to move on to the next level of our agreement, in accordance with the plan that our pastor had devised. He said that he would let me know after his vacation. I took my vacation at the same time as he did. Because he watched the baby during the day, I didn't have to pay for childcare. I went to Pennsylvania for about four or five days, and I didn't ask where he was going. At this point, I thought our relationship was on an upward trajectory. I would give him the space to think, and when he returned, we could progress to the next stage of our plan.

But after our vacations ended, Jake didn't return. He said that if things were going to continue as they were, he would not come back, would not continue with the contract that we had devised. I told him that I didn't want to get back together again until we ironed out all of our differences. I simply couldn't handle any more conflict. So, he chose to quit his job and stay where he was.

Chapter 2

Changes

After Jake decided to stay where he was permanently, the children and I were totally on our own. He did not want to work on our marriage, as I did. To me, reunification did not make sense without first fixing our differences. I did not want the relationship to be like it was, with Jake's constant infidelity and dishonesty. This is nothing upon which to build a relationship. I wanted to heal our marriage, to make a fresh start with new boundaries set in place for us to grow together as a family. He didn't want to do that work though, didn't want to help maintain our family. He did not seem to realize that building and maintaining stability takes work. He simply wanted to sit there and have his family without actually doing anything for us. I said I would not do that. We could not come back together unless we both continued with the program the Pastor Matt had outlined. I could not proceed in this marriage without healing it first.

The next three or four years were challenging. I was raising my children on my own, and I was facing the daily pain of knowing that my husband had left me. Most days I lived with a lot of anxiety and fear. I was worried about making it each week, worried about my children's grief, worried about how I myself would heal. This was a very difficult time.

The challenges were numerous, the obstacles plenty. One of the most difficult parts of all of this was childcare. I had three very young children. My oldest was eight, my middle child was two, and my youngest was just under a year old. Before Jake left, he had agreed to help care for the children. He said that he would watch them before I got home. Now, I was on my own. There was nobody. There was no shortage of childcare providers in my area; however, I couldn't afford any of them. Childcare is very expensive, especially when we were living on only one paycheck. Jake's leaving was difficult emotionally, but there was also the very tangible cost of his departure. The literal, financial cost. I went through three childcare providers in the span of two months.

The first childcare provider I went to recommended that I apply for childcare vouchers through social services. But through this process, my children were in her care for two weeks without the vouchers and I incurred a debt of $700.00. While this may be on the more affordable side of childcare, I still couldn't afford it. $700.00 was not readily available to me. I simply did not have the money. I did pursue the childcare voucher, but unfortunately, the information that the woman gave me was outdated. I could not be the recipient of a childcare voucher if I was not already receiving welfare benefits.

So, I moved on to a second option that I hoped would be more affordable, since it was closer to where I lived. This ordeal was even more unfortunate than the first. Isaac, who was still a baby, fell very ill. I took him to my pediatrician, who advised me that the daycare was what was making him sick. Of course, I wanted to withdraw him immediately. I couldn't send him back to the place that was doing this to him. But then, I needed to pay extra for withdrawing with short notice. Frustrated, I looked for another place. I enrolled my two youngest children in a program called Alpha Fundamental. This would have been ideal because they are excellent for early childhood education. Unfortunately, this place was too expensive too. I couldn't afford to send them there.

The childcare dilemma was at the forefront of my mind. Giving my children stability was important, and I had no choice but to move them from daycare to daycare. I was growing increasingly frustrated by this entire ordeal when my sister noticed the trouble I was having. I was fortunate because she remembered a woman who used to watch kids when my mother was still alive, and my sister managed to track her down. Exhausted from my previous attempts but hopeful about this one, I had an interview with her. She fit. I was so relieved that we clicked, and to make the situation even better, she didn't charge me an exorbitant amount of money for her care. She had known my mother and did me a favor. I was so grateful for this. Finding adequate child care was one of my biggest challenges and one of my biggest priorities. This woman worked well for us though. I stayed with her until Isaac graduated from nursery school.

It was also difficult to keep up with my children's education. I had two toddlers and a third grader to manage while still working full time. My days were packed. I came home in the evenings exhausted and overwhelmed, my nerves shot, and my body exhausted. I still had household chores to attend to, and I never knew where to start. The work was near endless. My oldest needed a lot of assistance with her homework. She had always struggled with focus, and now that her father was gone, schoolwork was the last thing on her mind. I don't blame her at all. This type of situation is difficult for adults, but it was even harder for a child to handle. She could not have been expected to cope with all that was going on and still maintain mental energy for her schoolwork without a lot of guidance. My Godmother came over twice a week to help her with homework. We were worried that with all of the stress, she would not be promoted to the next grade. The situation at home was consuming her. Her third-grade teacher told me that one day she left the room screaming, "he left us!"

Of course, this broke my heart. She was old enough to need to experience what was happening, but too young to try and make any sense of it. I couldn't even make sense of it and I was an adult. My oldest daughter told me that, at one point, her father had told her that he planned on leaving. I was incredibly upset that Jake felt like it was acceptable to share this information with a seven-year-old. Why would he put that kind of pressure on her? And to make it worse, she told me that she felt stupid for not saying something that would convince him to stay. My child had convinced herself that it was her fault that her father left. I told her that this absolutely was not true, but she was grieving in such a way that logic could not be delivered. Her father had left her. There is no place for logic in that.

Financially, I was struggling. I lost forty percent of my income when my husband left. This is nearly half, and I was left completely scrambling. Raising three children on my income was nearly impossible, and I had to dedicate even more money to childcare since Jake was no longer there to help. Those expenses, along with my overall monthly expenses, completely consumed my budget. There was absolutely no extra.

I live in New York City, where the cost of living is extremely high. It is one of the most expensive places in the world to live. When I married, I made the mistake that many married couples do: I didn't keep in close contact with my friends or family. I settled into the comforts of my immediate family, as well as their demands. They became my circle. My world revolved almost entirely around my husband, my children, and the church. This means that my other relationships were neglected, when in order to thrive they needed to be nurtured. I stopped giving them the resources they needed to grow. This meant that I could not turn to these relationships for support. I had to reach out to people who were once close to me, but who I had by then drifted away from. I wasn't even very close to my siblings. We all had our separate lives, we were busy. For the most part, we kept to ourselves. This made facing a crisis extremely difficult. I felt that I had no network.

The bible says that two is better than one, because if one falls down then the other can help him up. I was also discouraged by my church, because we were not taught to live by this philosophy. We were encouraged to be independent, not interdependent. I learned this term from Dr. Myles Munroe, who is a brilliant teacher and world leader. We are too separated, he says, we don't have concern for one another. We do not live as one unit, as one body. God uses people to bestow his blessings. We are the carriers of his goodwill. We should see God in one another. There is an Old Testament principle that was implemented by the Jews and carried over into the Christian church. That principle is tithes and offerings. The bible teaches, "bring ye all the tithes into the storehouse so that there may be meat in my house." But where was the meat? The church is meant to care for its people, to treat each individual as a valuable part of a spiritual body, but this isn't what I saw. There wasn't money for people who were facing a rough time. As members of a church, we should face obstacles together. Instead, I was left to face mine separately. Alone. There should be no hunger in the church, no lack. Our material needs should be met so that our spiritual needs are met as well.

I'm not suggesting that everyone in the church sell all their earthly possessions and give the money to the poor, but I do believe that a system needs to be in place that protects those who fall upon hard times. That is our duty to our fellow members of the church, to our fellow members of our religious body. We, as the body of Christ, should not have to look to social services for help, should not need to look to an outside entity to take care of our own. In the body of Christ, there should be no lack.

Emotions

Anxiety is a major byproduct of separation and divorce. I was worried because I did not know what the future held. As the non-initiator, I was taken off-guard by the separation. It would have been wise to put money away, but I did not know that I needed to. I never expected this, so I did not feel like I needed to save for a moment such as this. I was in a financial stronghold. It's not as though I wasn't preparing, but I was preparing for maternity leave by solidifying my business. I thought that this was the best way for me to prepare. I did not think that I had to ready myself for my husband's departure. While I was trying to move up in my company, to situate myself on a ground in which I could earn money while still caring for my baby and my body, all hell broke loose in my home. No amount of safeguarding could have protected me from something this unexpected.

While I was on track to becoming a director in Mary Kay Cosmetics, everything fell apart. I had a wonderful team and it looked as though everything in my business life was about to come together. But due to the stress of the impending abandonment, of what I dreaded was to come at the hands of my husband, my baby was born four weeks early. No matter how I tried to protect my baby from any shock as the result of my stress, our bodies react in these ways regardless. In addition, my team members started to get sick and our team was not the strong unit that it was before. Even before I knew that my husband was leaving, I tried to earn and retain some extra income. I thought tirelessly about the children, about the future of my family, but the world felt as though it was spiraling out of my control. Everything was unraveling to such an extent that our top director believed that the devil was infecting our group. The only thing we could do, she said, was to pray. Now I know that she was right. It was the devil.

I started getting anxiety attacks soon after I went back to work. It must have happened then because I needed to worry about the stress of finding someone to watch my baby while I was at work, and I needed to make sure that somebody could also watch my children when they got home from school. This is a lot to take care of, both emotionally and financially. I was eager to get back to work and earn a paycheck, but as I mentioned earlier my first paycheck was a third of what I typically make. I needed to use nearly all of it to pay the sitter, and I had no money whatsoever left to buy food. It was horrible. The sitter, wonderfully, took me food shopping. This experience was unbelievably humbling, as it always is when you need someone to feed you, as I learned in the upcoming weeks.

I attended church faithfully throughout this time, and there was a food pantry housed there. The person who ran it was incredibly kind and gracious, offering this food to me. He told me only to worry about paying my bills, and that they would fill my refrigerator. This is what I thought a gesture on behalf of the church should look like. It was a way to make sure that our hungry bellies were filled, that each household had enough to eat. And with their help, we did have enough to eat. The first time they gave us food my daughter's eyes widened as she said, "we are rich." Tears puddled in the corners of my eyes as I thought, at least in that moment, "we are rich." We had more than enough to eat, and we were filled with the kindness of those who had provided for us. I had more after Jake left than when he was there. The Lord had provided when my husband refused to and when I could not.

The Lord also covered for me. The people who ran the food pantry were discreet about giving me food. We met subtly, in different locations. This was above and beyond what they needed to do. They could have shaken their heads at me and told me to wait in line on Saturdays. But they didn't. They could have given me a box of food and sent me on my way. But they didn't. They provided me with an abundant supply, with a wealth of food and the material support that I had been seeking. I am forever grateful to them, to those hands that fed us when we were hungry. They acted as the Lord wants us to act.

These gestures eased my stress. Without wondering what my children were going to eat, I could worry about how to pay the rest of my bills. I could worry about providing them with quality care. The world underestimates how a full belly can provide us all with the momentary reprieve we need to make it through the challenges in our lives, the sustenance we need just to keep going.

A lot of people ask why I didn't just go to social services. Social Services exclusively helps those below the poverty level, and I was not below the poverty level at this point. I have a job, and on paper, I make good money. But losing forty percent of my income when my husband left dealt a very serious blow to my finances. I could not easily recover because the bills were still the same. I was not eligible for food stamps, and they no longer offered childcare vouchers. These were the two services that I most needed. Unfortunately, you can't qualify for those services with a certain income. Fortunately, I had my church.

Chapter 3

Make Me Your Dwelling Place

I suffered for a very long time, for a number of years. The financial stress was unceasing, ever present in my day to day life. It was exhausting and my nerves were shot. I was at my wits end, unable to engage with my life in a truly meaningful way. So, I went on a fast because I know that you hear more readily what the Lord is saying, and His response is quicker. Isn't it funny how we will wait until a situation is unbearable before we consult the Lord? So, I fasted for one day and he gave me a dream.

In the dream, I was in the church for a service. During the service, the pastor brought me a young woman and asked me to minister to her. *Make me your dwelling place,* I sang out to her in a sweet, clear sound. *Make me your dwelling place to dwell.* I woke up and immediately recorded the song. I knew

73

everything about the song, as though God had placed it in my chest for me to speak it lyrically. For me to fully understand it. I knew that the song was meant to be sang both in Spanish and in English. I recorded it, thinking about what it meant. "God, why did you give me this song?" I asked.

I thought about my fast the day before, and about the intentions that I carried in my heart. The Lord was asking me to make Him my dwelling place. He had provided me with the answer through the song that I sang in my dream. He was making it clear through the dream that I had. He pointed the scripture John 15:5 out to me, which reads, "I am the vine, ye are the branches: He that abideth in me, and I in him, the same bringeth forth much fruit: For without me ye can do nothing."

Despite the clarity of the dream and its message, I was still uncertain as to what the Lord was telling me. I just didn't fully understand because, the truth was, I did abide in him, so I thought. Constantly, I was at the church every time that door opened. I was very active.

I sponsored all night prayer meetings and headed an auxiliary. Was this not abiding in him?

It would take me a few years of contemplation to fully understand what he meant by "abide in me." The Greek word for "abide" in this scripture is meno, and it means to remain, stay, wait, not to depart, to continually be present. In this scripture, Jesus Christ of Nazareth speaks to his followers, comparing our relationship with him to a grapevine. He says that He is the true vine, and that God the Father is the husbandman. We are the branches, but we cannot bear fruit in and of ourselves. In order to be fruitful, in order be branches that produce fruit, we must abide in Him. In other words, we must be connected to Him. Without that connection, we are simply dead. We will never produce the fruit that we are meant to produce.

As a born-again believer, I thought that I was connecting with Him. I thought that I had solidified that relationship. In order to better understand this analogy, and to begin connecting to Christ in the way I felt that He was telling me to, I started to study how grapes grow. Learning the depth of this scripture and truly exploring it would provide me with the answer I sought. In my search, I learned that grape vines must grow for three years before they actually produce fruit. They need well-drained soil and plenty of sunlight. They also need a lot of care. If they are not regularly pruned, they will have more shoots than they will buds. When this happens, the foliage is so immense that it does not allow the sunlight to reach the grapes. Then, of course, they will not grow. Like the parable of the grapevine, if we do not stay connected to the vine, to our source of all life and production, then we will not be fruitful. I continued to do research, and I stumbled upon a site that linked the scripture John 15:5 with Psalm 46:10. Throughout the course of this journey, I began to realize that "abiding" equates to "stillness." Emotional stillness. When we are wavering in our belief in God we are doubting. The Bible says that no man shall receive anything from the Lord if he doubts. With the worrying I was experiencing; my faith definitely was fluctuating.

The scripture Psalm 46:10 says, "be still and know that I am God." The Hebrew translation of "still" in the scripture translates to "let go." Not only letting go but letting go and focusing on God. The preceding verses describe a war, and through the war God instructs the person to be still and to know that He is God. Stop and let go, He says. Have the faith necessary to rest with confidence in His presence. I still wasn't sure how this related to my reality though. I understood the scripture more, analyzed my reading in greater depth; however, I still couldn't make the connection with my own life.

One day, I was listening to one of my mentors and she talked about remaining emotionally still. From what I understood listening to her speak, I realized that I was allowing my emotions to take me out of alignment with God. My emotions had not been still since Jake left, and they were in disarray even before that due to his infidelity and spousal indifference. I felt like I needed to fix everything, to scramble for stability and to provide for my family. I was constantly worried, constantly stressed. I was depressed. A dwelling place was not a physical location, I realized, it was a state of being. Is it within the mind, present in our emotions? Being and abiding in God. The question was, "how do I create this state of being?"

This state in which my emotions aren't all over the place. This sense of calm in the midst of a storm.

Chapter 4

Stillness (Abiding in God)

When God first revealed to me that I needed to abide in him, I was blown away. I thought that I was abiding in him. I attended church frequently. I was near constantly thinking about God or so I thought. I think more like mental gymnastics. I was a minister, a leader in the church. If God was my focal point, I wondered, what more could I do to abide in him? For him to tell me this was a surprise. I felt like I was in Him, that I was dwelling in Him. But as I learned with the Grapevine, the fruit will always show where you are spiritually.

The situation with Jake had left me fruitless, barren. I was, in a sense, rootless because I was not focused on God. Or, I did not have my sense of God in the right place. Because of that, I was worried, anxious, prone to panic attacks. My inner strength was minimal, nearly nonexistent. I blamed myself for my situation and fretted over it constantly. Even though my financial predicament was a byproduct of my separation, I couldn't help but feel like I had gotten myself into that situation. My situation consumed my life, blocked the light that God wanted to provide.

When the Lord told me to "abide in Him," according to John, Chapter 15, I was a little clueless. I wasn't fully aware that he was referring to my relationship with Him. They were blocking me from receiving guidance and instruction from the LORD. Fear was controlling me. I was performing duties or tasks for the LORD, but I was neglecting spending time with the LORD. There is a major difference between attending Church and spending time with the LORD. We can get caught up in attending Church and still neglect our relationship with the LORD. It was about our closeness. Relationships must be built, nourished, tended to over time. Trust is never automatic. Knowing does not happen right away, but rather is a process. It takes a long time to truly know someone, to understand the intricacies out of which this being is built. It's the same way with our relationship to the Lord. If we aren't close to Him, we spend a lot of our time wrapped up in darkness. In that room of our darkness we cannot hear Him, cannot make out what He tells us beyond our own clutter. The cares of our lives block the Lord from reaching us when we need Him to.

The Lord told me to draw nigh to Him. So, as time went along, the Lord started to show me that abiding in Him would only develop once I habitually spent time with Him. The Bible says in Romans 12:2, "but be ye transformed by the renewing of your mind, that ye may prove what is that good, and acceptable, and perfect, will of God." This means that you can't change behavior from the outside in. True change comes from the inside out. I need to try and eradicate my own clutter, to tend to the vine that would lead me to Him. According to Psalms 46, Verse 10, stillness is basically letting go. It's about learning to rest with, and in, by totally focusing on Him.

We can learn to rest well with our Lord only through stillness. This, in my vernacular, is really prayer. But it's not praying as we have grown to know it. Very often, we think of praying only as an appeal to God, a way to ask Him to fulfill our wishes. A prayer reads like a laundry list of what we want God to do for us. Maybe our "to-do list" for God is noble, maybe our requests meant to be good. But we rarely take the time to wait, the time to listen. We don't rest in His presence and focus in on Him, who is the vine.

The Practice of Prayer

I love to use a certain prayer book by Christian Word Ministries. It is an awesome prayer book because it doesn't pray your feelings. It prays the Word of God. This is important, because praying implies a certainty that God hears your prayers. But to get assurance out of prayer, we must pray His will. We cannot pray outside of His will and expect favorable answers. It is the Word of God that will spiritually build us up, that will give us assurance that God hears our prayers. It shows that we are open to Him, that our interest rests with His will.

The Art of Stillness

I have, through my journey, managed to acquire the directions on how to achieve stillness. Stillness is acquired by entering into God's presence on a daily basis. It's not only acquired by being in God's presence but what you do while you're in HIS presence. One of the major results of practicing stillness is achieving emotional equilibrium. Frequently, whether we are experiencing a traumatic situation or not we have a tendency to fluctuate between belief and unbelief. This is due to the conditioning of our subconscious mind which overtime has been conditioned to respond to certain situations in certain ways. It is called emotional memory. We all have programs running in our subconscious mind that dictates how we respond to every situation. We don't even realize that this is

You can liken these programs to ~~gnolds~~. A stronghold in this sense is place where a particular cause or belief is strongly defended or upheld. Therefore, when you have wrong belief systems in place that have resulted from past experiences they have to be dismantled. This is only done by spending time daily with God, rehearsing over and over again His word in order to create new pathways in the brain. The inability to stand assured that God is a loving father who truly cares for us is largely based on past negative experiences which makes us expect the worse. However, whatever the reason for us not being able to stand assured that God hears us it can only be remedied by drawing near to Him. The Bible says in Hebrews 10:22, "Let us draw near with a true heart in full assurance of faith, having our hearts sprinkled from an evil conscience, and our bodies washed with pure water." The Bible also says in James 4:8 Draw nigh to God, and He will draw nigh to you. Cleanse your hands, ye sinners; and purify your hearts, ye double minded.

My anxiety and my worry were fueled by my inability to truly trust in God. I was experiencing so many rapid changes and my faith was literally nonexistent. Being that my world was turned upside down it was as if I was expecting the next avalanche or monsoon to hit my life. It was literally making my nerves bad. So, this inability to believe God would answer me was hindering my prayers. I wasn't resting in Him. I didn't have a true solid inner knowing or peace that comes as a result of spending time with God.

The Bible says in Hebrews 11:6, but without faith it is impossible to please Him: for he that cometh to God must believe that He is, and that He is a rewarder of them that diligently seek Him.

When something happens, maybe it is something traumatic or difficult, a particularly long and hard struggle, do not make it your first reaction to worry. Don't become anxious or impatient. Don't have a panic attack. Know that deep from within, there is peace. You can readily talk to God within your inner man, your spirit man. Your first response should be not to respond outwardly, as we have been taught to do, but rather to respond inwardly. This is abiding in God.

The ability to respond this way has to be developed over time. For me I had been shaken to my core. I had to be built back up again in my inner man. Jude 20 says, "But ye, beloved, building up yourselves on your most holy faith, praying in the Holy Ghost." I had to enter into the divine presence of God by spending time with Him daily and reestablishing my relationship with Him. A relationship not based out of fear but out of love.

Faith based on covenant

Close your eyes and take a moment to imagine that you are standing in front of The Temple. When I say The Temple, I mean God's dwelling place in the Old Testament. This place was sacred, incredibly dedicated and holy. Let me describe it to you: Outside, there is the outer court. There, you enter through a gate to where anyone is able to congregate. Then, you have the inner court. This is where the priests come and wash their hands and feet in a brazen laver before sacrificing their offering at the brazen altar, in order to purge people of their sins.

Next, the priests take coals from the brazen altar and enters into the Holy Place. There, they offer prayers before God with the incense from the golden censer. They fall prostrate on the floor with their shoes off and worship God. In the Holy Place, there are two other articles: The Golden lampstand and the Table of Shewbread. The lampstand provides the only source of light. The priests needed to make sure that the lamp always had oil. It could not go out, because it symbolized the illumination that only God could give.

In the New Testament, this illumination is Jesus Christ: "He is the light that lighted every man that comes into the world" (John 1:9). The Shewbread Table contained twelve cakes, and these twelve cakes were eaten by the priests on the sabbath and replaced each week. They symbolized our necessary dependence on God. "Give us this day our daily bread," the prayer goes.

Then, we have the most sacred place: The Holy of Holies. This is where the Ark of the Covenant dwelt, it was the sign of the covenant that God made with Israel. The Ten Commandments are inside the Ark of the Covenant along with the golden pot that had manna and Aaron's rod that budded. The Ark of the Covenant had a golden lid which was considered the mercy seat. The high priest entered and sprinkled the mercy seat with blood once a year to atone for the sins of the people. This was meant to appease the wrath and anger of God for past sins committed.

Now that we know what this place looks like, what the Dwelling Place visually represents, we must ask, "how do we enter in with God?" According to God's biblical pattern, in the old testament (Exodus 25 through 27), our heavenly father set forth a pattern for the tabernacle, which he would indwell, the place of worship and coming to know him." Today we are that tabernacle and we can dwell with the holy spirit. The place of worship is within us. We are the temple of the Holy Ghost according to 1 Corinthians 6:19.

Most people think that a place of worship must be formalized, that it must be a physical place or building where we can collectively lift hands, where we can sing to God. I used to think that as well, that as long as I was regularly attending church, that my relationship with God was complete. But true worship is an intimate relationship, an exchange that takes place between you and God. Today we are that tabernacle and the Holy Spirit dwells within us. The place of worship is in our hearts. No physical building will ever be as intimate a gathering place as our own selves.

"But oh, I know how to worship already," you may be thinking. That was me, too. I knew how to worship already. I was in church all the time, was a major presence in the physical gathering place around God. I lifted my hands in song, in praise. I was devoted. I really wasn't thinking that I wasn't spiritually strong. It nothing like a major loss to show you stable you are in your belief. But the truth was, I wasn't developing our relationship. I realized, and I want others to realize, that the number of church activities you are involved in, the amount of time you spend in church, does not alone allow you draw closer to God. While these activities can be beneficial and wonderful, and they can make you closer to your church community, they cannot substitute what you need to do to draw closer to God. He is the vine and we are the branches, and we cannot grow or properly be sustained without him. There are no limits to our growth with the Lord.

Forgiving God

I would like to address an issue before we go on to address developing the art of stillness. For many of you, because of a dramatic loss or traumatic event you have faced, you may not be open to God. You may have a lot of questions as to why "He has allowed" this event to happen to you. He understands that you are hurting, and it may be difficult to seek out intimacy when we have been hurt by intimacy in the past. It is easier to remain guarded, closed. But developing a relationship with Him will allow you to counteract your fears, your worries, and to help you through the Valley of the Shadow of Death. When you're ready, God will be there. He is always there, and He is always ready. He is only waiting for you.

He will never hold your current feelings against you. Right now, you feel bad, you feel depressed, you are always upset. But God is there to help you, to send others into your life to help you. Do not stay in those dry places for too long, those barren and isolated places of pain. Reach out to Him. If you stay in those dry places for too long, you can and will get stuck there for a very long time, way beyond the time that you're supposed to be there. Those places are not hospitable to growth, or to love.

Grieving is not a place where we're to live, it is a place that we pass through. Passing through grief is inevitable but living in it is not. I know that escaping feels unimaginable right now, and you can't picture yourself developing this art, mastering the ability to seek stillness enough to escape. But that is because you're still in those stages of hurt, overwhelmed by your feelings of grief. But God is waiting for you. He's there. He knows how you feel and can help to absorb some of that pain. He nudges you, gently reminding you that you are entitled to your pain, but you should not remain controlled by it for too long. When you're ready, His hand will be extended towards you, reaching for you, eager to pull you out of where you are sitting cloaked in your own darkness.

Fight or Flight

The part of the brain called the Amygdala is responsible for our so-called "flight or fight" response.

It's considered our fear memory. While it is responsible for our response to threat, it cannot differentiate between a real and a fake threat. Studies have shown that with prayer and meditation, there is a decrease in brain cell volume and a change in our subjective perception and feelings. Essentially, a new pathway is created in the brain that allows our response to stressful situations to change for the better.

As we continue engaging with God, we will notice subtle changes. These changes occur while we are in our prayer closets because we are meditating on and speaking the Word of God. It's essential that we do this on a daily basis. Consistency is key. Remember you are creating a new pathway in the brain and that requires repetition.

This is where we transform from our old selves, with our old habits, our old ways, and begin transforming into a new being with Christ's character, His nature. Now, an exchange takes place. The default mechanism that was once in place, that person you used to be, the way you used to think, the emotions you carried around with you, will start to change. Your brain will expand, new pathways will be created that allow you to operate from a different perspective. Your default mechanism will not be to fill your days with worry, to succumb to anxiety, because now His Holy Spirit is taking over your being.

Now you're being filled up with the Lord, not with worry or pain. Not with material or other attachments. You are not filling your spaces with drugs, food, alcohol. The world's vices are nothing to you. Even simply going to church, going through the motions, is not enough. I thought that because I was going to church that I was depending on God, that I was leaning on Him. Instead, I was just trying to forget. I did not yet know what a true relationship with the Lord looked like.

I remember when I went to church only to forget. I went to praise God, which distracted me from my worries. It allowed me to, momentarily, forget about the problems that I was facing. Instead of facing the problem, instead of dealing with what I needed to deal with, I was in church jumping up and down, shouting, praising God, living a fantasy. It was all to keep myself from remembering the pain and the turmoil that I was experiencing. It was a time when I felt that I could forget about my finances, when I didn't have to think about my mounting debt or my bills. Now don't get me wrong praising God can be and is therapeutic.

This was dangerous. I didn't deal with the problems in the ways that I should have. As a result, they grew progressively worse. I refused to look at my issues, hoped that they would simply go away on their own. God doesn't want that for us. That's not what he intends for us to do with praise, to use it as a tool to forget. God is a God of your entire being, He wants you to be whole and well. I was not recovering properly. I was not recovering properly at all.

You must build up your relationship with the Lord, build up your inner man during these trying times, because there will be forces that come against you. And when they do, as they inevitably will in this life, you have to be in a place, in a posture of prayer, to handle them. It takes time for the Lord to develop this within you, and you can't use any other vices as distractions from that. You can't use people or things as crutches. This will lead to unhealthy relationships, poorly founded attachments.

I would encourage anyone not to rush. Pastors, leaders, lay people, need not rush to fill voids with unhealthy relationships of any sort. It's important to first build up a healthy support system. This way, you won't make your decisions based on loneliness and neediness. This is always a mistake. You are capable of again being whole, but only if you take your time. Allowing God to fully restore you, so that you do not attempt to fill your life with the things that don't benefit you.

I will again speak of stillness. Stillness is letting go, it's being still before Him and knowing that He is there. Psalm 46 is all about war. There is destruction all around, it is plaguing the person who is writing.

The situation is bleak. Then, the person hears from God. And in the midst of their turmoil, and in the midst of their trauma, God says to them "be still. Just stop what you're doing. Stop trying to fix it in your own way. Stop trying to fix it with your own might. Rely on me. Let me show you that I am God.

Let him show you that He is God. When I was having trouble with childcare, for example, I was switching up babysitters every couple of months. I could not find the stability that I craved and that my children needed. I just could never find the right fit. Now can you imagine if I had stopped and consulted with the Lord, how my situation would have been resolved much sooner? Then, my sister came like a messenger to tell me about Ms. Butler. "Look," she said to me, "we need to call Ms. Butler." Ms. Butler was a blessing. She had been watching children for a very long time, and we knew one another's families well. I'm so grateful that my sister was able to track her down. Through her, I finally found the stability I had been seeking. She was our sitter all the way up until my youngest started school. While I had once been changing sitters every couple of months, I was able to stay with her for a couple of years.

What I learned from this is that when we stop trying to fix a situation, and we allow God to step in and handle it, it will all work out much better. While our vision is limited, He can see all things and knows all things. Nothing short of that will work, you need Him. People live entire lives without ever recovering from trauma, because they have not turned to God.

Fully recovering means stepping back into your full capacity, back to the self you were before the loss. We lose a part of ourselves when we experience loss. We stop functioning fully, stop operating as we should, and we grow stagnant. But I want to fight against stagnancy and I want you to, too. I want you to make God your dwelling place, and I want for you to dwell in Him. Don't find a substitute. Don't depend on work, alcohol, food, or anything else to fill your void. Only He will make you whole again.

Often, we try and replace those lost things of our lives in unhealthy ways. It's the only way that we can think of to truly replace them. But the truth is, a substitute will never be the real thing and it will never replace the real thing. A substitute teacher may do fine, but he or she will never be your teacher. God does not want you to have a substitute. He wants you to have something entirely new, entirely real.

God wants you to have something different, something new and better in place of what you lost. But we don't want to wait. We want the immediate gratification, but ultimately unsatisfying, sensation, that a substitute offers us. We will never get our former spouse back; our exes may never again be ours. We might never have the job that we had before. We will never get back what we are trying to substitute for in the first place. That's because we are choosing substitutes that are not God. And only He can give you something that will be just as good in the original's place. Let us never again rely on substitutes, but to allow God to fill that void with authenticity. He will fill our void with something new, something different. Amen.

Environment

When you're trying to achieve stillness, you need to create a specific place dedicated to that. I chose to go to the same place at the same time every day, because I came to think of that space as a place dedicated purely to the Lord. I've heard people say, "we're not trying to be religious, but we want to have a relationship." Of course, we want a relationship, but as in all relationships, as in all that is worth dedicating oneself to, we must establish consistency to make it work.

If you're a person who goes to the gym, then you know that consistency is key. Every day, you try and go to the gym at the same time. You develop a weekly routine and maintain dedication to that routine. Maybe you warm up in the same way. Maybe you make sure to eat the same thing afterwards. You might switch up the workout, but you go to the gym. You are attached to that routine. The same concept applies to establishing stillness. You make it a habit to go to the same place every day. There, you pray. You meditate. You focus in on God and establish the relationship that you have with Him. And every day, you continue to build that relationship up.

This is the only way to grow properly in the Lord because He is our source and without Him, we will not grow properly, and this is how you will ultimately fill those voids. There is a song by Tasha Cobbs that goes "Fill me up Lord, until I overflow. I want to flow over, Hallelujah, I want to flow over." You're building resilience and character up in you. You're building up his Holy Spirit in you, to take away the anxiousness, to take away the worries, the struggles, fears and replace them with His peace.

God will help us through those situations, because now our focus, our look, is not to man, it's not to our flesh, it is only to God. We form a daily reliance on God. At first, I strongly suggest that you create a prayer closet. I would like to give you a scripture in reference to prayer closets. Matthew 6:6 says, "But thou when you pray, go into your room and when you have shut your door, pray to your Father who is in the secret place; and your Father who sees in secret will reward you openly." Now your prayer closet can be any place, so long as you and a few others can go and not be disturbed. The prayer closet should be in a secluded place, yet it does not need to be completely devoid of noise. Your time with God is your time with Him, and you should avoid distractions so that you can fully engage with Him. You don't want your phone in there. We must detach from the material world in order to fully feel Him. You don't want to allow your mind to wander, to get sidetracked. Once you've established the place, once you've removed your distractions, you can focus in on God.

According to the prayer book *Christian ministry*, there is a pattern to approaching God. If you are familiar with the Old Testament, you know that God had a set way for the priest to approach Him. One of those ways is to wash before we enter into the presence of the Lord. We do that by confessing our sins, and repenting, and asking for forgiveness. The Christian Ministry book says, *"You need to get rid of every stronghold. Demonic spirits, sins, bondages, wrong prayers, assignments that come against you, and unrighteous agreements have to be destroyed. Any controlling prayers, instruments of unrighteousness, evil principalities, powers, and rulers in high places need to be severed from you. You have to be cleansed by the blood, and have the armor of God on, when you enter into His presence."*

"We will enter His gates with thanksgiving in our heart. We will enter His courts with praise. We will enter the Holy Place." This is what we must consider as we bring ourselves to stillness in the spaces, we have created for ourselves. In the Holy Place, if you know the tabernacle, there's the shewbread, which is Jesus the Bread of Life. He is life, where the candlesticks of light, or illumination, are. The Holy Spirit brings to us knowledge, wisdom, revelation, understanding. He is the light of men and women. The altar is a site of true worship and exchange. It is

here, in this place with Him, that a deep and true intimacy can occur.

Then according to the Christian Ministry book after you pray, get cleaned up, and ask the Lord to let loose angels about you in the house, it is the time to enter in. Typically, it is best to begin by speaking to the Holy Spirit. "Holy Spirit," you can say, "I ask you to pray to my Lord in heaven." Lead me and guide me into the Holy Place, and then into the Holy of Holies. In the name of Jesus, I command my spirit, mind, will, my emotions, ego, libido, imaginations, subconscious areas, the mind of the flesh, and all other areas of my life, down to the obedience of Christ within me.

Once you have quieted your mind and begin to focus intensely on the Lord and become focused on your intentions you can begin to formulate your prayer. You should begin a with a prayer of thanksgiving. I like to practice gratitude when going before the Lord. When you begin to thank the Lord for everything in your life from your children, to your home, job, family members, friends you become more away of the fact that there is no lack in God. God is a God of abundance. Everything He does is abundant. For example, if you look at the trees they have so many leaves and branches. What about the strawberry? Look at the abundance of seeds on its skin. Look at humans. Men are born with millions of sperm and woman are born with an abundance of eggs. For what purpose you ask? So that we can be abundant and reproduce. God created us this way. We are abundant because we serve an abundant God.

So when you come before God with the perspective that there is no lack in God your prayers are different. You're not approaching God out of neediness and wondering if He will answer. You have an assurance that He will answer because He has already supplied you with everything that you need. Just look around you.

You will now approach Him with confidence and your prayers will be less about you and more about Him and others.

As you continue to pray daily and focus more on God you will develop more sensitivity in your spirit towards God and this will open up lines of clarity and establish what I like to call a "flow". What I mean by a "flow" is that the issues and desires that are on your heart will begin to gravitate towards you. A mother at my church always says that prayers are magnetic. We don't understand the power that we possess in our prayer closets. There is so much available to us through God's word that when we start to apply it things start to happen. Change takes place. The problem with us is that we don't put our faith and belief into practice. Like they say practice what you preach.

Thank you, Lord, yes Lord. Thank you, Lord, you are the bread of life, and you are the light. You are the candlesticks of light, the illumination, the light of the Holy Spirit. Bring us life and light, wisdom, insight, understanding, revelation, and realization. Hallelujah. I enter a phase of utmost praise and adoration. This is a type of prayer. It is incense lifted up to our heavenly Father.

I get so excited knowing that God is taking me into His divine presence, that I am before the Holy Place, that I am in this Holy Place, and I am before His throne. He hears me. And I know that here, and now, He truly hears me. He knows about this situation and I do not need to plead for him to make it work out in my way. I know that he has an answer and that the answer is Him. I know that I will be well. "All is well," I can then say.

Now that we are in his presence, we are there to hear Him. We are there to feel Him, and to know that He is eternally with us. Hallelujah. There is no separation. This is the best feeling in the world. This is the best place to be in the world, and we honor Him because of it. I am so excited. We serve an awesome God. He is the Lord of all things.

As the bible says, "In Him we live, and move, and have our being. There is nothing outside of Him. He is all encompassing, He is all knowing, He is all powerful." Hallelujah. He is in every place at all times. When we are with Him, there is no space and no time as we traditionally know it. There is no separation from Him. I can feel His presence now, as I'm writing this book, writing this for you, because I want you to experience the greatness of His presence. I thank God for His holiness. I thank God for His presence. And I thank God for His deliverance in your life. Amen.

After I established the mechanics of stillness, I needed to fully understand the kind of emotional state that I was in. First, I knew that I needed to grieve in relation to myself and that I needed to grieve in relation to my children. This was absolutely crucial for me to achieve, because managing the intensity of my emotions was a necessary step in achieving the mechanics of stillness. Grieving has to do with your emotions, about your response to particular situations. Because my children and I had both been abandoned, I needed to grieve for them as I needed to grieve for myself. I was hurt because of what happened to me, but I was also very hurt because of what they, in all of their innocence, were going through.

After the Lord revealed to me that I must make Him My Dwelling Place, he also began to reveal details about my emotional state. One night I was sitting in church when a Sister requested a prayer for someone who was experiencing The Valley of the Shadow of Death. I had heard the phrase before, but I realized that they were referring to the stages of grief. Previously, I had been ignorant as to its full meaning. I had actually not considered the phrase in all of its possibility until that point, but I soon found out that my mentor, Dr. Keller, had given me the answer eight years earlier.

I did not know that this box I had received so many years prior had the answer that I was seeking. By this time, Dr. Keller had passed away, but the Lord looked ahead into the future and provided me the answer through one of His loyal servants. I didn't know it when she gave it to me, but the box was full of materials pertaining to how to handle the stages of grief. She gave me the box in case I was to return to counseling school, but after a certain point I no longer considered that a possibility and left the box to sit unopened. I was tired of school, I thought. I will not be enrolling anytime soon. So, eight years after she gave me the box, I finally opened it. Little did I know the materials would mean so much to me personally. This box is how I became familiar with the term "The Valley of the Shadow of Death."

While I didn't know that my answer would be presented to me in this box, my heavenly father must have. I didn't even open it for myself, initially. I opened it for a friend of mine who was dealing with depression. I sincerely hoped that its contents would help her. I opened the box and saw that there were a number of materials pertaining to loss, and one book was titled specifically "Recovering from Loss."

I opened up the book without expectations, still simply hoping to help my friend. But then I flipped to a page that contained a diagram, and at the bottom Psalm 23:4 was written. This was the first time I had seen "The Valley of the Shadow of Death" in relation to grieving a loss. This could not be by chance. This was another example of the way that God sent messages to me, the ways that He made my own healing process available to me. Eight years prior, God had gone into my tomorrow to place this box in my closet for the time He knew I would need it. I was in my own valley experience. This was what I needed for that, and for my friend's valley experience as well.

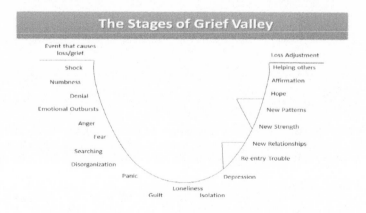

This chart was an awakening for me, because it allowed me to see where I was at emotionally. I saw, visually represented, all of the stages of grief I had already passed through. I also saw the stages that were still to come. According to Wiktionary, "The Valley of the Shadow of Death" is a symbolic description of the world, meaning that darkness and death are (symbolic) valleys on earth one must walk through. It is part of the experience. We must all, at one point or another, trudge through these valleys. Nobody is immune to pain. But we must all remember that our God will get us through. Yea, though I walk through the Valley of the Shadow of Death, I will fear no evil: for thou art with me; thy rod and thy staff they comfort me. Psalm 23:1-2.

While walking through the Valley of the Shadow of Death is not easy, it is possible. It is made more manageable if you or another person is able to identify where you are in your journey. This map allows us to know that an escape from that valley is possible. That the end of our darkness is always within reach.

Chapter 5
Valley of the Shadow of Death

Defining Loss

Loss is the state or feeling of grief when deprived of someone or something of value. Often, we don't even realize that we are grieving. Our grief affects us at a much deeper level than we often thought possible. We all acknowledge it in different ways, and we do not always understand the process behind our grief. All of this raises the question, what is grief? Grief is deep, enduring sorrow caused by the loss or impending loss of anyone or anything that has strong emotional value. What is of value to us differs depending on who we are. We will not all grieve the same, and we will not all grieve for the same thing. A number of examples of what loss looks like can be found in the Old Testament. If we take a look at the scripture reference in Genesis 37:34, and it reads, "Jacob tore his clothes, put on sackcloth and mourned for his son

113

many days." Here, the word for grief is "Abal," which means to mourn or lament

Another word for grieving can be found in the the New Testament, which is 'Lupeo,' which is to be made sorry. This comes from a root word meaning pain of body or mind. The scripture reference is Matthew 17:23, and it reads, "They will kill him, and on the third day, he will be raised to life, and the disciples were filled with grief."

There are many stages to the grieving process, and when we are individually going through this process, we do not always know that we are stuck in one of the stages. Grieving is a process, and we hit each stage at different times depending on a number of factors. We all take our time differently; however, as I said previously, it is important to avoid stagnancy. I am going to outline the stages of grief for you, and these stages are also known as the "Valley of the Shadow of Death."

We will start off with the event that causes one to grieve. Obviously, each case is unique. We all face different struggles within our lives. In my situation, I needed to grieve over my marital separation. At first, I didn't even know I was going through the grieving process. As a result, I could not form logic with what I was experiencing. I could not identify the stages that I was going through. I was simply going through the motions of my life without any real intent.

If you look at the image on the previous pages, you will see the first three stages of grief are as follows: Shock, numbness and denial. When we first begin grieving, it may not feel like grief at all because we are in a state of shock. Shock is a sudden, upsetting, or surprising event or experience. Basically, whatever is the impetus to our grief leaves us reeling. There was no way that we could have prepared for this. Shock can also cause numbness, which is emotional detachment. We don't yet know how to respond to our situation, so we're attempting to remove ourselves from the pain before even experiencing it.

You may have heard someone say something along the lines of "Oh, I don't feel anything. When I see him, it doesn't even bother me." Most of the time, this is a lie. Not an intentional lie, but a self-preserving lie that allows the person to feel like he or she doesn't need to grieve. Usually, the person simply is not ready to face what has happened to them, so they begin to detach from the situation entirely. Facing it feels too painful.

This leads up to our next point, which is denial. Denial is the act of declaring something to be untrue. Basically, your mind refuses to accept the reality of what has happened. It's a way of coping, but of course it has no permanency. This often happens when somebody loses a loved one. Sometimes, people can't fully accept the fact that this person they loved, and who they still love, is dead. It may not be until months later when they finally accept the fact that the person is truly gone. Denial hits people in various ways. People can be in denial about credit card debt, for example. But very often, it involves loss and coping, because denying that they must grieve will always be easier than grieving.

The next three stages are intertwined. They are emotional outburst, anger, and fear. We start to slip slowly down the slippery slope that will lead into the Valley of the Shadow of Death. It's inevitable, but it is perhaps the most painful and difficult part about grieving. You may not necessarily experience all of these parts to the grieving process, but you will likely experience some of them. And when you do, it is helpful to be able to identify where you are and what your specific symptoms are so that you can effectively deal with your emotions.

An emotional outburst can be read almost as a breaking point. It is a sudden and violent release or outpouring. This can take different forms depending on the person. It could be tears. And it may not be as a direct result of what you are actually grieving from. It can be a broken glass that brings on the tears. It may even look like you're crying for no apparent reason. You could have anger, a strong feeling of annoyance, displeasure, or sometimes complete hostility. Maybe you lose your temper over something completely insignificant. When you can recognize this as a stage of grief though, you will know that you're not actually crying over nothing. You are beginning to grieve, and this is important.

At some point in our lives, we've all experienced fear. Fear can be paralyzing, both physically and emotionally. Fear makes you afraid to move, afraid to progress. Fear can be defined as an unpleasant emotion caused by the belief that someone or something is dangerous, likely to cause pain or a threat. At one point, I personally had a lot of fear. I was afraid of the unknown, afraid of a future I never planned. I was afraid for the psyches of my children. I was afraid that I would not be able to take care of them. My fears were endless, consistently daunting.

The next three stages are searching, disorganization, and panic. I personally experienced the horrific sensation of panic attacks. My heart rate would escalate, my breathing would grow labored and heavy. There was one instance when I had to go to family court to fight for child support. It had taken me a full year to track down my then husband in order to serve him with papers. While at the courthouse waiting to see the judge, my husband sat down across from me. He glared at me, intimidating me with his gaze. My throat felt like it was closing, like there was no way I could get air. I knew that what I was doing was right, but I still felt like my world was spinning, that my body was panicking out of control.

I sent a text to my pastor, asking him to pray for me. I explained to him the physical sensations I was having, and he kindly responded, telling me that I needed to up my prayer game. He was right. Panic attacks come on suddenly, whether because of a threat that is real or imagined. We can ask ourselves why we are having these physical sensations, especially when, like in my case, I had no doubt that I was doing the right thing. We experience this searching behavior, wondering why we are having sensations such as this, why our bodies are responding in the way that it is. Our thoughts then wander to the source of our panic, to our loss, and we begin to blame ourselves, or we begin to ask so many questions about the incident. Our mind rolls constantly with questions that may or may not have an answer. "Why did this happen to me?" I remember asking myself. "What was he doing? What was the real reason that he left me? What did I do?"

I could never find any reason that was good enough, or bad enough, to justify his leaving me. That never stopped me from searching though. I always wanted to know why. Sometimes, an answer will never be available. My husband gave me reasons for leaving me, but none of them held any weight. They simply could not have been true. Some people get stuck in their grief because they never find the answer. They must accept that a good answer just is not there. But you cannot allow that to be a hindrance.

The next stage is disorder. It is the possible disorganization and disunion of emotional distress. Your order system breaks up. It seems, a little bit, like chaos. What was once a cohesive whole now feels like the breakup of constituent parts. The break up begins internally. We feel like our inner worlds were shaken by whatever loss it was that we experienced, and now this rupture transcends into our outer world. In my case, my home became extremely disorganized.

I used to be an excellent housekeeper. I was clean and immaculate. But once I went through my separation, I became increasingly disorganized. I could not keep any regular system of organization. There was absolutely no order to my home. What was once tidy and manageable, was suddenly cluttered, filled with disorder. Partially, I was suddenly busier. Not only was I emotionally distressed, but I had a baby and two young children. What work was once divided by two was suddenly forced onto one. And unfortunately, I didn't have anyone to step in and help me. I was the kind of person who went to church, work, and home. My immediate family, my husband and my children, were my constant occupation. Because of this, I really didn't have much of a support system in place. I was entirely on my own.

The next set of three is loneliness, guilt, and isolation. I was already lonely because I really didn't have any close friends. I really wasn't that connected to my siblings. I do have three sisters that live with me here in New York, But I was not connected to them in such a way that I felt like I could call on them for any sort of help. This was part of the downfalls of marriage. Our networks begin to feel so tight that we don't extend beyond them. Our immediate family feels like enough. So, I also did not have a circle of close friends, and this group of people outside of your family on whom you can rely are so important. Especially if, like me, you are a loner. I was a bit of a loner in that, outside of work and church, I really did not socialize much. I kept more or less to myself.

Even now, I often choose to stick to myself. But I've gotten better because I have intentionally created a circle of people, a network on which I can rely if I have a problem. So, my social isolation has been somewhat remedied. The next emotion is guilt. I have not experienced much in the way of feelings of guilt; however, I did feel guilty in the sense that I felt I may have let my kids down. I had never wanted my children to be part of a "broken family home." But then, they were. And I wailed inside for them. I wailed for them deeply.

Very often, people tend to retreat into their own silent corners and suffer silently. That's what I did at first. I tried to handle everything on my own. I wasn't doing so intentionally, but that was the way I was raised and that is how we are taught to react culturally. We're raised to be independent, and so in being independent, I isolated myself. Also, it is not uncommon to crave alone time when we are going through something extremely difficult. Studies demonstrate that this is true. You're not in the mood to deal with other people, not in the mood to let them see your vulnerability. You may even feel embarrassed or ashamed of your situation. Fear and pride can be one of your biggest hindrances from receiving the help you so desperately need.

James 4:2(b) of the Bible says, "ye have not, because ye ask not." I find a lot of truth in this statement. We will not ask because we're afraid to ask. So many people are afraid to reach out for help. We don't want to give off the impression of transparency, to let others know that we are in pain. That's the bad part about going through the "valley of the shadow of death." We won't seek help when we need it. What I have realized from being the one hurting is that, as believers, we cannot see that someone is hurting and not offer comfort. The Bible instructs us to bear each other's burdens and so fulfill the law of Christ (Galatians 6:2). We are to mourn with those that mourn, it says. Sometimes though, we don't know how to approach a person who is silently suffering. We are afraid that we may cause them more harm than good. But if the Holy Spirit leads you to do or to say something, please don't hold back. That person may be craving comfort, and you may be just the one who can provide them with that. You are the very one that the Lord wants to use in order to bring some form of consolation to a person experiencing loss.

The darkest moment during the Valley of the Shadow of Death is called depression. Depression, according to psychologists, is anger turned inward, trained onto the person experiencing grief. It is, essentially, a condition of internal gloom, dejection and withdrawal. One of the signs that a person might be depressed is that, such as with my own case, they separate themselves from other people. They grow further from their peers than ever before. Additionally, their environment is very often a mess. A person who kept an immaculate house before the traumatic event struck may suddenly have a house that looks very much unkempt. Or, a person who was once very concerned with personal hygiene can now scarcely maintain standards of presentation. These are all signs of depression. Other signs are that a person may not be sleeping, or for others the sign could be overeating or not eating regularly enough. All of this fall within the symptoms of depression. Unfortunately, those at church will often tell you, "Jump up three times, turn around, clap your hands, shake it off." While this is sometimes the answer, it very often isn't. And telling others that they should be better when they are not yet capable of getting there through easy means can do more harm than good.

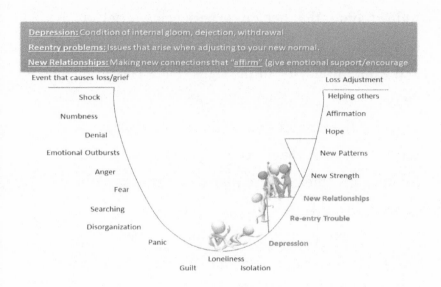

Depression: Condition of internal gloom, dejection, withdrawal

Reentry problems: Issues that arise when adjusting to your new normal.

New Relationships: Making new connections that "affirm" (give emotional support/encourage

The Bible does say He will give you a garment of praise for the spirit of heaviness, and it will lift you out of your troubles. But it is also up to you to identify your depression and to force yourself to become more aware and conscious of your symptoms and the impacts these symptoms have on your life. It's like you're in a deep sleep and need to be shaken out of it, need help snapping out of it. Some people get stuck in this depression and see no way out. They remain locked there, often for years and years and years.

These people need help getting out of their depression. They cannot see light on their own, so they need someone to show it to them. If you isolate yourself, if you keep yourself from reaching out for help, you feed your depression. Because the enemy loves to attack us when we're alone. When you're in a group, you have support, you have stability. But when you are alone, you're weak. So that's when the enemy plays tricks with you. When you're by yourself. So you can stay stuck, you can stay wounded and depressed, and you can remain rooted in your own darkness. What you really need though, is to come out.

You could finally be emerging from this for many different reasons. It could be because a friend came to you, or because now, the Holy Ghost is descending down to give you the nudge that you need. Maybe the Father has sent His Spirit to gently wake you, to make the lightbulb in your brain light up, to make you recognize that right now, you need help. "I have to get up out of this place," you might say. Or, "I can't stay here," "I am doing things wrong," "I am letting myself go," "I'm not eating properly," "I am stressed out," "I am overwhelmed." You may form these words in a variety of ways, but what they all ultimately mean is "I need help." Furthermore, what's important is that you are finally saying, "I need help."

It is in this moment when you look at the diagram at the bottom, when someone comes to your aid at last and begins to pull you up and out of your darkness. This is never easy. Emerging from this place will never be easy. There is always the issue of reentry, which we will discuss later. Issues will arise when adjusting to your new normal. Remember, you emerged out of the darkness in a different place. It does not mean that everything will be the same as before. It does not mean that you will have back what you once lost. But it does mean that you will have begun recovering. I will use myself for an example. When I went through my separation, things changed drastically. I went from a two-parent household to a one-parent household. And this was a huge transition. While caring for two children would have been difficult in and of itself, I was also left with the shock of caring for a new baby. I was pregnant when all of this transpired, and as a result, so much changed. I went from having two children to care for with the help of my husband to having three children to care for without his help. I worked full time, and still had to make sure that everything ran smoothly at home. It was quite an adjustment. And, I could not have done it by myself. If there were not people there to support me, if I did not have people there at different junctures, at different stages of my transition, I would have not come out of it. Like I said, we are most vulnerable when we are alone.

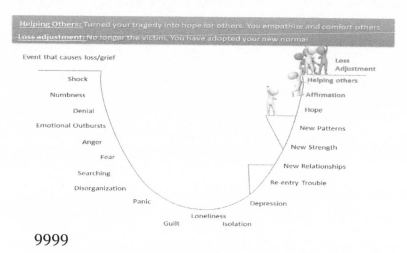

9999

The stress was taking its toll on me, and it transcended my mental state and made its way into my physical appearance. I simply could not control my own physical self at this point. My hair fell out in droves and was beginning to gray prematurely. It was as though the aging process was exacerbated by my circumstances. I lost weight, which made me look sickly. Truly, I was. I was sick, sick with grief, sick with depression. Parents at my children's school stared at me, started commenting that I "needed to take care of myself." Or, "Wow what happened? You lost weight." My abdomen began to protrude. I initially thought that this could be baby fat, which would make sense considering I had given birth to three children, one quite recently. But I talked to a personal trainer, and the trainer told me that this was a side effect of the stress. It's amazing the information that people can get about you if they have the information, the way that people can read us if they want or need to.

This trainer coached me through different exercises, and one day I very nearly passed out during my workout. I wanted to maintain some sense of physical routine amidst all of this, but I couldn't. My body wouldn't let me. "Are you on medication?" The trainer asked me. "If not, you should be." The trainer was concerned, was concerned about my physical state when I did not have time to be. This was a wakeup call of sorts. I realized that I badly needed to get myself together, needed to stop my mind and body from completely wasting away. It was a brief moment of clarity, a glimpse of my situation from a professional perspective. Of course, as they often do, that moment of clarity faded.

Taking care of ourselves is always of crucial importance. God looks at the whole man. Not just the spiritual side. He wants us to be healthy, happy, whole individuals. He did say, "I wish above all things that you be in good health and prosper even as your soul prospers." Some preachers believe that he doesn't care about our happiness, but he does. When I say "happiness" I don't mean that we have everything that we want every single day, that everything goes our way all of the time. Struggle is a part of life. But I do mean that the Lord wants us to be stable and content.

There are so many elements that are important to our overall well-being. We need to maintain a proper diet, need to rest well. We need to exercise, at least a little bit, with some regularity. Getting good sleep and maintaining the appropriate attitude are vital towards maintaining a sense of wholeness. No one area can be out of balance, or else it will throw you off course. While I was experiencing my stress, I developed a stomach ulcer. My stomach was completely out of whack. I also experienced a nagging pain in my side, and the doctors did not know what it was. I was so paranoid that visits to my gastroenterologist became typical. So typical, in fact, that I was becoming a nag. She had to refer me back to my primary care physician.

Emotionally, I was hurting. I needed to be healed. Before I could be healed physically, I needed to be healed emotionally. It was simply that the arduous effects of my day were impacting my overall health. It was like the time I went to court, and my throat felt like it was closing up because my ex-husband was there, staring me down. My pastor was right when he told me to up my prayer game, because I was experiencing a panic attack. While the physical symptoms were very real, it was all a result of my emotional state.

I have a number of anecdotes that illustrate this point further. For example, one day I was at work and I was walking down the stairs. I had walked these stairs countless times, knew where each step was and how many there were. But one day, I missed a step. And I hit the ground. As I sat there, wondering what happened, my co-workers all said some variation of "looks like someone needs a vacation." This was a mild version of what I needed at that point, but I did need a vacation. I was run down, and I desperately needed a break. I could not keep up with my daily demands in that state that I was in. So, I sent my two oldest children down south for the summer. This was helpful. I loved them, but I needed a chance to allow my mind and body to rest. They needed a complete recovery. In stressful situations, we do not feel as though we are allowed to rest, but this is when we need it most.

There were other physical ailments that I experienced. At one point, I needed a biopsy because I developed two lumps in my breast. It was one difficulty after the other. While the lumps may not have been connected to my situation, there is no doubt that physical health is drastically impacted by our emotional state. Then, it only adds to the stress. Permanent physical damage can be done as a result of this stress. We must be weary of this.

But the goods news going forward is that once you start to cultivate a daily practice of spending quality with God, you will begin to heal. God will start to change your very nature. Your default mechanism will begin to dissipate and a new mindset will develop. There's so much that goes on in our secret closets that you can't even begin to understand. You will actually begin to feel the difference within yourself. What the Bible says about being transformed by the renewing of your mind is literal. The daily repetition of going before the Lord transforms you at a cellular level. Sometimes we view scripture theoretically and not practically. The strategy that I have outlined in this book will change you at your very core.

Chapter 6
The Butterfly Emerges
(Purpose, Identity, New Normal)

After enduring the Valley of the Shadow of Death a person starts to reestablish themselves. There's a scripture which says, after you have suffered a while, may the God of all grace, who hath called us into His eternal glory by Christ Jesus, make you perfect, establish, strengthen, settle you. When the Lord starts to fill you up, He will begin to replenish you and refurbish you. You will start to again gain a sense of purpose. This is important because, for some of us, we've experienced a great loss. This loss, whether directly or indirectly, affects our purpose. Often times, we are tied to a person, a place, or a thing. When that changes, our entire lives can be upended. Our whole purpose transforms from something that we thought we knew into a different path entirely. This impacts our function in life, our reason for being, the very thing that gives meaning to us.

When your purpose is impacted, you lose your bearing. You lose your stability in life, what you thought was your reason for living. While our reasons for living can transform, if we have dedicated our lives to a narrow set of reasons (as most of us have), then our worlds will inevitably be shaken. After a loss, it feels like our purpose has been tarnished. But then, at some point, the Lord begins to situate things in our lives and He brings us back into alignment with Him. Now, you are capable of looking up at Him and that is when you realize that you do have purpose. God gives you a new identify, which is refreshing and powerful. This is absolutely something to love. Who you are, your very being, is redefined. "Who am I?" You may begin to ask yourself. "Was I the pastor's wife, or am I simply me?" You need to learn how to live and to be. You are being, being in Him.

If we can achieve that, this state of being, then we can flow better with God. We will flow with Him endlessly, contentedly. We would move in and out of situations much easier because we carry this world as a light garment, something we take off till we put back on. Now, you might think, I have a new purpose in life, a new identify. I am re-emerging. It is a rebirth. A new life created with and in God. You come out of that hole, out of the pit that your situation forced you into. I know now that I have a new normal, a new life, new habits, new friends, and a new environment. Everything is healthier.

It is always easier for a person to recover from loss when they have purpose. And that is why loss is so hard to recover from. You felt that you were robbed of your purpose. But if you can create a purpose and a goal that is not related to any mortal person or thing, then it is much easier to recover from loss. It has solely to do with you, and that is perhaps the one thing that you can control: yourself. At the end of the day, you control your own behavior. You are responsible for your own actions. But you cannot control anybody else. You will never be able to control anybody else.

For me, this journey towards creating my own purpose has been an awesome journey. I never would have arrived here without horrific loss; however, I now listen to myself. I hear my voice when I speak. Healing has been brought into my life through the flow of living water proceeding from God the Father. This healing and these words flow into you like waters of life. My voice comes to me when I speak. I get deliverance, healing. Why? Because He is in me. Greater is He that's in me than He that is in the world. I do decree and declare that God is great and He's closer and He's nearer to you that you know, if we only understood that. That's why you can speak.

You can speak to your mountains and say mountain be thou removed to the midst of the sea. You, I think, you might not even have to believe it, but if you hear it, yes. Faith cometh by hearing and hearing by the Word of God. Speak life, speak peace, speak to yourself, God is in you. Yes, He's in you. He's in you to deliver. He's in you to heal. He's in you to give you peace, peace that passes all understanding.

In writing this chapter I am reminded of the butterfly. From the time the butterfly is birthed as caterpillar he goes through nineteen changes. Meaning he sheds his skin nineteen times before he actually becomes a butterfly. We often look at our Christian experience as beginning from the time the caterpillar goes into the cocoon and emerges with its beautiful wings. But in actuality the Christian walk begins from the time the caterpillar hatches out of its egg and as a Christian in our development we will go through many changes before we emerge as that bright and colorful butterfly. We have to keep growing and learning by feasting on the Word of God which is the bread of life. We have to remain in God so that when life throws you different twists and turns you have the capacity to bounce back.

I don't know how it works, exactly. But I do know that it works. Faith is more than a feeling it's knowing. You know based on what His word says that you can overcome. I know it works. Hallelujah. Thank you, Jesus. I can speak to my life. I can speak to my circumstance. I can speak to the atmosphere. Hallelujah, in my mind, there can be change. There can be peace. There can be love. There can be joy.

The Bible says in Romans 14:17 For the kingdom of God is not meat and drink; but righteousness and peace, and joy in the Holy Ghost. Lord God help us to find that space today. Help us to find that place today, in you. Help us to make you our dwelling place. Oh God, not figuratively, but literally. Yes, Lord, in the name of Jesus, bring the wisdom, bring the peace, bring the stillness to our lives, to our situations.

Change our perspective so that now, we can re-emerge. We can be born again in the name of Jesus.

Take Care of Yourself

"Take care of yourself," a parent from the PTA (Parent Teacher Association) said as he passed me in the hallway. On another occasion, one of the mothers gave me a look mixed with pity and shock. "You look deathly," she seemed to say, with her eyes. One of the women at my church who had not seen me in a while touched my cheek, looked sad for a moment, and told me that I had lost so much weight.

I was not taking care of myself. I looked constantly run down, and for a while, it got worse every day. My cheeks caved in, looking always gaunter. It was about two or three years after my separation, and I was a mess. Due to the extreme stress I was under, my hair was falling out in patches. I tried to cover the hair loss by wearing my hair natural, but none of the looks were flattering. Truthfully, at this time, no look was flattering. I was simply deteriorating rapidly. The stress took its toll in my body in a rough sort of way.

As I have previously mentioned, my stomach was protruding. What I thought was still weight from giving birth to three children, was actually a symptom of the stress I was feeling. It was that day at the personal trainer, the day when I almost passed out, that made me realize just how stressed I was feeling. And how much I was carrying that stress physically. I was on the treadmill when it happened. I got lightheaded and thought I was going to pass out. It wasn't just being out of shape, it was that I legitimately could not carry myself. I went into the bathroom and laid down on the cold floor in the fetal position, trying desperately to make the dizzyingly sick feeling go away. When I emerged from the bathroom, the trainer did not ask me to work out again. Instead, he pulled me into the office and sat me down. He explained to me that he could tell that I was heavily stressed. And not only because I nearly passed out on the treadmill, but also because I only carried fat around my midsection. When a person carries the bulk of their body fat around their midsection and not carrying fat in other places. It's a bodily reaction to stress. He told me that if I continued to work with him, he would change my perception on life.

This allowed me a moment of clarity. That conversation allowed me to see my life as it was. And, honestly, it was a mess. My body was falling apart, but it was falling apart because of my circumstances. "You need to get yourself together," I thought to myself. That moment of clarity didn't last long. I still had a lot of emotional work to do before I could reshape myself, so to speak. But that moment, even if it was that moment, was so crystal clear. And why? It's just exercise, some might think. Why did this trainer feel like my workout routine was going to change my life? Research has shown that due to the raised endorphins that exercise provides, the brain experiences temporary benefits. Exercise impacts serotonin and mood, alleviating symptoms of depression. Basically, it is important to maintain our bodily temple. It is connected to our psychology and neglecting our physical self will make recovery more difficult.

Exercise can help with the recovery process, facilitating certain mental changes that allow you to begin to think more positively. There is so much living to be done, and we can't live abundantly if we don't take care of ourselves.

Steps to Living a Healthy Lifestyle

You may wonder how to start living a healthy lifestyle. It's easy to feel overwhelmed by this. It's a good idea to start with a visit to your primary care doctor for a physical. It's important to have your blood drawn so you will know of any deficiencies the body may have. For me, I was constantly exhausted. But I thought it was because I was a single parent raising three children. But in all actuality, my iron was low. As soon as the doctor prescribed me the pills meant to reverse this, I almost immediately felt the difference. Additionally, an iron deficiency causes hair loss. So, something as simple as getting my blood tested and taking an iron supplement allowed for an immediate boost in my health. Finally, I had energy.

In addition to my iron, my vitamin D levels were also low. The doctor prescribed me to take 50,000 iu of a Vitamin D supplement per week for two months. Vitamin D affects your mood. Vitamin D is produced from contact with sunlight. But if we don't have access to the outdoors in the ways that we should, we can easily become deficient. This is why many people suffer from seasonal depression in the winter. A lack of sunlight, and therefore a lack of mood-regulating vitamin D, can have very serious effects on people's mental health.

One day, after picking my children up from an after-school program, they wanted to go to the park. I said no, because I was on a strict schedule at the time, and I did not think that we had time for something I had deemed frivolous. But my oldest daughter turned to me and said, seriously, "Ma, God meant for us to enjoy nature. You need to stop and smell the roses." My daughter was right. Out of the mouth of babes, I thought. This was exactly what I needed to hear. I never took time to enjoy the outdoors, to feel the sunshine on my face. I thought I was too busy. But maybe I wasn't busy with the right things. I was always rushing, never taking even a minute to breath in some fresh air. There are so many benefits to communing with nature. First, it's shown to relieve stress. It also helps you perform tasks better, making you more efficient with those tasks you neglected the outdoors for in the first place. You exude more positive emotions, experience less anger. You have greater life satisfaction and better health. All of these benefits simply from taking a walk outside. Your well-being truly does benefit from this.

Daily Nutrition

Anyone who has experienced a major loss knows that it affects your diet. You may not have an appetite, or you may crave unhealthy foods because of the comfort that they can provide. Or you may simply not have the emotional energy to prepare the food that your body needs. But in order for the body to operate at its optimum capacity, it has to be provided with proper nutrition. Your body is like a machine, and all machines need fuel. Food is our body's fuel. When I first faced my financial issues, I would get my food from the church's food pantry. This was certainly a blessing. Without them, I would not have had the food I needed to get by. My children and I would have gone hungry. But the problem with food pantries is that the food is often not of the highest quality. It is usually the food other people don't want, a lot of canned goods and non-perishable items. Even on the best days, there was a lack of fresh produce. And this is one of the most important elements to living a healthy lifestyle. Without it, deficiencies will inevitably develop.

Often times, we don't have too much of a say in what we eat because of our situations. This was my case. Sometimes we're too busy to prepare fresh and healthy food, or sometimes we simply can't afford the investment. But when we can, we absolutely should. We should make this a priority. And along with a proper diet, it's smart to take multivitamin, vitamin D, and omega 3. These are all essential to your overall health and well-being. These vitamins, along with the proper diet and exercise, will help to combat the depression and anxiety that can so easily creep into a poorly-nourished body. It also doesn't hurt to limit your caffeine intake. According to the Medical Daily, caffeine appears to be linked to anxiety and depression. Of course please consult with your doctor before taking any vitamins.

In addition to proper diet and exercise, proper rest is crucial. Nothing ages you faster than a poor diet and lack of rest. The term "beauty sleep" is accurate. Sleep makes us look and feel refreshed. So, it is absolutely necessary to get that "beauty sleep." Sleep is one of the essential building blocks to your overall wellbeing. For example, sleep helps to improve memory, increase your lifespan, lower stress, and to diminish levels of irritability associated with depression. Of course, the benefits are really quite endless; however, I'm focusing on the benefits in relation to loss. I want to focus on how being healthy can help alleviate, and even reverse, the downward spiral that we tend to enter into as a result of loss. If you have to go through the valley, I don't want you to get stuck in the valley. There are ways out.

We have a journey ahead of us and we don't want our physical bodies to adversely affect our recovery in any way. While I know that depression is often circumstantial, and we can't always control our circumstances, I also know that our body is a temple that is connected to our spiritual selves. When we pray, when we make the Lord our dwelling place, we shed our physical selves. But when we are out in the world, we need to maintain the physical bodies that the Lord provided to us. We should not maintain our physical health out of vanity, but rather out of reverence for the Lord's creation. We are the Lord's creation. We must never forget that.

Emerging from the Valley of the Shadow of Death

As time passed and I continued to walk closer to God by spending more time in His presence I began to notice that certain situations and scenerios that bothered me before didn't have an effect on me anymore. For example, early on during my separation I attended a marriage retreat. The pain of my separation was still fresh and I ended up leaving the retreat early because I couldn't bear to listen to the presenters talk about how divorce is wrong and so forth. Now I am an on staff counselor at my church and I provide marriage counseling. I have a totally different mindset. Another example of my reemergence is that I am more in tune with my purpose. My focus is about my personal mission in this life. Whereas, before I was basically performing church activities. Now I know more about who I am and what I am here to do. Last but not least the worry and anxiety that I used to experience surrounding my finances is no more. I know that I have a heavenly Father who loves me and that He knows what I have need of. He's an excellent provider. Glory be to God. I have learned so much these last few years that I believe I would have never attained if I hadn't gone through this struggle.

I did not think I would ever emerge from this Valley, or that I would ever make myself financially stable again. I had lost forty percent of my income, meaning that I was constantly struggling. I was the only provider for my three children. Not only did my income decrease, but my family size increased. Isaac was a brand-new baby when my husband left. I had another child to provide for and nobody to help me to provide. The stress of this situation was unbelievable. I was constantly worried, constantly worried about how I was going to provide adequate care and material resources to my children. Of course, the Lord provides for all things. After various childcare providers, I finally found the right fit. After worrying about how I was going to feed my children, the church helped me to feed them.

During this time, I neglected my children because I was neglecting myself. I could not get out of bed, could scarcely interact with the world in any meaningful way. The world had crashed down around me, why would I want to interact with it? It took me a very long time to realize that taking care of my physical self would make my emotional self feel better. It was not the whole part, but it was a piece to a large and complex puzzle.

What truly allowed me to recover and improve was Making God My Dwelling Place. Throughout the mess and the chaos, this is what truly increased my clarity. At one point, I was looking for a second job. I felt like working more hours would allow me a greater sense of purpose. During the Christmas season I applied to a job at a retail store. After a group interview, they called to offer me the position. I thought very seriously about accepting, but those in my immediate circle made the point that it would be difficult to take care of three children while working two jobs. My life was already strenuous enough, and my time was already limited. I didn't know if I could leave my children home alone for that long. I wasn't entirely convinced that the money would be worth the sacrifice, but I did need money. I needed to figure out what to do. Or, I thought I needed to figure out what to do. But really, I didn't realize the answers were right there the entire time.

I needed to listen to God. Once I did this, once I Made God My Dwelling Place, my clarity increased. It increased because I took the time to truly hear God. One day I was sitting at work, and it occurred to me that I could increase my exemptions on my payroll deductions. I had started at that job eighteen years prior, when I didn't have children. So, I claimed zero exemptions. Instead of taking a second job, I simply needed to take that money from the exemptions I deserved anyway! The money was already there. God, I thought, why didn't you tell me this before? He did though. I just wasn't quiet enough to listen. I was too riddled with anxiety to receive a clear word from the Lord.

I also noticed a distinct difference in my physical appearance. It began to improve once I Made God My Dwelling Place. I put on the weight that I had lost, and my hair grew back. Due to stress, I was experiencing baldness in the front corners of my head. I went to the dermatologist for cortisone shots, which can help hair grow back. I told her that stress was the cause of my baldness, and she told me that if I did not manage my stress, that they would not work. Luckily, I had remedied my stress. I Made God My Dwelling Place. This made my stress more manageable, and my hair grew back.

Because I was happier, I was able to eat more. I was able to return to a healthier weight. I felt genuinely satisfied. After I made God My Dwelling Place, I was in a more consistently contented state. I was relaxed. I went out more, developed new friendships. My life, which was at one point a blur of stress and sadness, again took shape. It was new. I was new.

I also began to notice that, after I Made God My Dwelling Place, that there was a flow. While before, every step felt heavy, now I could move along less reluctantly. Sometimes, things just worked out. That's what I mean by flow. Some people call this luck. Some people call it a good day. But it's more than that. Romans 8:28 says that all things work together according to His purpose. Situations I would fret over would easily resolve themselves. Many of my fears started to dissipate.

It was all because God came alive in my life. I started to understand what belief and faith truly were. I always thought that I was a woman of faith, and to an extent I was, but I had never before put myself so totally in God in this way. He was My Dwelling Place. Prayer has become vital in my life. I now know how truly having a relationship with God is so fully essential.

My kids even noticed a difference. My oldest said that 2014 was the year of change, the time when transformation truly occurred. I came alive. Previously, I had been so overwhelmed that I could not fully take notice of my children. I was struggling emotionally and financially. When I changed, when I truly focused in on the Lord, I started doing more activities with my children, started to eat meals with them. Of course, there were still struggles. Struggle will never fully go away. But what was different was that I was listening to God, I was making myself quiet for him. And because of that, I could again see life with its little celebrations.

It was during this time that I realized that I needed to interact more fully with my children. It was that day at the laundromat when I began to see them with higher levels of clarity. I was simply so happy that we were all together. That we were out as a family. This is when I realized that I needed to better tend to my babies. They are precious, and I am forever grateful for their presence. For their role in my lives. I had been experiencing diminished parenting during this time. I did not think that I could possibly take care of myself and someone else at that time. My emotions were so heavy, so hard to handle. I simply could not acknowledge them.

I soon realized, with the help of many other messengers of God, that better tending to my children would help me to recover, and that they deserved better parenting from me. They too had suffered from Jake's actions. They no longer had a father. They experienced a massive loss, just as I did. When I began connecting with them on a higher level, our family grew whole once again.

Spending time with my children allowed me to realize that without Jake, we are still full. We may no longer fit what I thought my family would be, but we are still a family. I can provide for my children in ways beyond the physical. I can make my home a nurturing place for them, a place in which they know the glory of God and the love of our home. Recovery was a long road for all of us, but we are stronger and happier as a unit than we are apart.

There are so many elements to seeking out recovery. Some of this is physical. It means taking care of ourselves, of our physical needs. We must exercise and eat good food. We need to nurture our bodies. We must also take care of ourselves emotionally and spiritually. This means spending time with our kids, spending time within our community, building up these strong networks that allow us to thrive. At the center of our recovery is the Lord. While the other elements are important, if we do not keep God at the center and recognize that our recovery exists with him, then none of our other efforts will connect. The Lord is the center from which all else extends, including recovery.

I managed to make it out of the Valley of the Shadow of Death. In our lives, we will all experience grief. We will all experience loss. We will never be immune from pain. While it is not possible to avoid the Valley of the Shadow of Death, it is possible to make sure we do not linger there for too long. If we make God our dwelling place, if we recognize that all will be done through him and in him, then we will emerge as we were meant to. The Lord's love is good, and it will guide us. In God, all things are possible. Deuteronomy 31:6 says, "Be strong and of good courage. Do not fear, nor be afraid of them. For the Lord your God, He is the one who goes with you. He will not leave you, nor forsake you." With the Lord, you are never alone. You will emerge from the Valley of the Shadow of Death with His help. Never lose faith. You will emerge.

Chapter 7
Diminished Parenting

Additional Resources on Diminished Parenting

My ability to parent was strongly impacted by my situation and was not fully remedied until I made God My Dwelling Place. Because parenting is such an important task, I have included additional resources on the Diminished parenting that comes as a result of high stress and trauma.

"Mommy," my child yelled to me, "can I have something to drink?"

"Yes," I responded absently, "bring me the juice out of the refrigerator."

I poured the juice while lying in my bed. They brought me their cups, brought me the juice out of the refrigerator, and scarcely lifting my head, I poured their glasses. They brought the juice back to the refrigerator and returned only to grab the cups that I was holding.

At the same time, I received another note from the teacher about an incomplete homework assignment. And then another note about lateness to school. I was always a good mother; however, at this time, I suffered what could be considered diminished parenting.

"Divorce creates an increase in parental role strain leading to a period of "diminished parenting." It is not uncommon for mothers (w/ whom 90% of children reside after divorce) to become self-involved, erratic, uncommunicative, non-supportive, and inconsistently punitive in dealing with their children. These mothers are also less likely to be successful in nurturing, controlling, and monitoring their children."

This parental strain usually starts when the separation begins and can last well into years after the divorce is final. This phenomenon can be compared to weeds in a garden. Once weeds begin to grow, they will spread swiftly. Unless somebody plucks them out at the root, they will spread rampantly throughout the garden, ruining the good seeds that have been planted. If weeds are left to spread, they will take hold of and choke the good plants. Eventually, the garden is overgrown with the weeds and the good plants have no space left. The garden scarcely stays a garden at all. It takes a good gardener to prune and care for the garden. It takes consistency. In this allegory, the gardener is the parent or parents, and the plants are the children. It is the parents' job to ensure that the children in their garden (home) are well nourished emotionally, physically, and spiritually. When a parent is going through an emotional battle, it inevitably affects the children. This neglect creates an environment in which weeds (bad attitudes, disobedience, lasting emotional baggage) can grow and completely take over the time. The weeds thrive, while the plants suffer. If not handled properly, this can last indefinitely.

I personally didn't realize that I was experiencing diminished parenting. One night, however, I was researching online, and I stumbled on a website that talked about exactly this. I read the article and said to myself, "this is exactly what I've been experiencing." I was so engaged with the battles I was facing in my personal life that I didn't realize I had put myself in a stupor. And unfortunately, my children were being dragged into it. My daughter made a comment that, until recently, I had not taught them anything. I hadn't taught her how to ride a bike or how to roller skate. The truth is, I was in such a state of blurred pain and worry that I neglected the basic tenets of outdoor childhood activities. I would take them to skating parties or to visit relatives and it would become clear that they were so far behind what could be considered typical outdoor activities. It's because I wasn't spending time with them.

As a family, we never went anywhere or did anything. We went to church. I went to work. We spent most of our time at home. I'm fully aware that I, alone, could not fully control this reaction. I was in such a state of disarray from the separation, and my emotional and physical states were deteriorating. I don't want anyone in this situation to blame themselves, because dealing with the trauma that we have had to endure is not easy for anybody. However, this doesn't mean that we don't need to make every effort to shake off these repercussions and to rewire the way we operate. We owe it to our children to try our best to do that. By Making God your dwelling place you will begin to learn to live in your present and not in the past. When you do this, you will not worry about the future. You will be fully there in your present and for all of those who exist in the present with you. You can gradually regain your awareness, to watch the fog that had been surrounding you dissipate.

Lucidity will finally begin to set in and the clouds will lift. Your children, like mine, will say that this is the year of change. They will feel it, recognize it as the moment that their family feels whole again. They will realize that their parent is again present. And they will be happy for it. 2014 was the year of change for me. I began to rebuild myself, to finally regain my focus. It wasn't easy. I came up with a lot of excuses, a lot of reasons for why I should not remain present in my own life. My life was too painful to be present, I once thought. It was impossible to fix the damage, I thought. But although it happened gradually, it did change. God sent people into my life to show me the light, and to help me to change my environment. These people helped me to restore discipline in my children's lives. It wasn't easy, as the saying goes, but it sure has been worth it.

I remember one day. It was bright and sunny, glorious outside. I insisted to my children that we all walk to the laundromat together. Sarah, my six-year-old, and Isaac, my four-year-old, had their scooters and helmets and rode along the road. Jenna, my twelve-year-old, helped me carry the bags. It was a menial event, a small task that everyone must attend to. But that day, something was different. We were together, walking or rolling on our scooters, breathing in the air that the day provided. We were actually excited about going to the laundry. In only about five minutes, we arrived at the laundromat and my oldest helped me load the washing machines. My middle child also wanted to help, of course. They worked together to load the white clothes in one machine and I put the dark clothes in the other. I instructed Jenna on how to load the detergent, where to put the fabric softener.

All of this is menial, but in that moment, everything meant so much. It meant so much because I knew that something was about to change. While the clothes were drying, I stood outside the laundromat and watched my youngest two roll back and forth on their scooters. They were having so much fun, taking in the sun and getting exercise. It was pure joy from them, in that moment. My oldest was a little disgruntled because, at twelve, she generally prefers to stay home and watch a movie on her kindle. But I wanted everyone with me. I had left her by herself for too long, she needed to accompany me, and I needed to, more often, accompany her. With my three children there, at a place so simple as a laundromat, I was on top of world. I was suddenly ecstatic because I realized that it was a beautiful day and I had my children. It was time to be present, and right then, right there, I was. And from that day forward, I would continue to be. I would be my best self and a better parent to my children. I am forever grateful for those who showed me how to be present with my kids while enduring a divorce.

One person, in particular, was helpful in that she explained how I needed to essentially re-calibrate myself. This person made me realize that I needed to do a lot of work in order to effect change in my kids' lives. Controlling their behavior required me to change. Controlling the situation was relatively simple. I needed to be present. But of course, being present is not actually always as easy as it sounds. It can be nearly impossible when one is forced into the unpleasant situation of dealing with depression and extreme stress. To some, to those who have not had to live through a traumatic situation such as a divorce or death, it may seem like I am being irrational. That I am harping on something insignificant.

But it is not insignificant. To children, a parent's presence is vital to their well-being. And while I was there, I was not actually there. They were suffering because of my internal uproar. Because I was trying to navigate my own loss, I could not help her. She was left to suffer alone. My youngest was behind academically, and he did not talk as well as he should. He was born in the midst of all of the chaos, so I did not work with him often at home. I did not talk with him, did not always interact with him in the ways that I should have. He knew nothing in pre-k. He didn't know how to write his name and he didn't know how to sit in class. Because the necessary guidance and structure was absent from my home, my children suffered.

There is a scripture in the book of Revelations that says, "Be watchful and strengthen the things which remain..." After I realized that I needed to be more present in my kids' lives, the lord impressed this scripture upon me. Through this, I realized that I needed to strengthen those things that still remain. My children were what remained. So, I needed to focus on them, needed to build them up. They needed me, and the impacts were noticeable. As soon as I started spending time with them, they started to fully blossom. The change in them was swift and obvious. We became closer.

Children in households that have undergone an abrupt separation or divorce also face more behavioral issues than children who have not had to deal with this. They are more likely to fall victim to delinquency and are more likely to engage in impulsive behavior. This means that they are more likely to engage in substance abuse and to drink alcohol earlier. In addition, their academic performance is often negatively impacted.

Children also deal with loss differently than adults, and for my children, their father leaving was a profound loss. Children often experience poor performance in activities that they once loved, or they tend to cry frequently. They develop high levels of anxiety and are afraid of unreasonable things. The children will occasionally lose interest in childlike play, growing into adults well before they should. Their self-esteem often suffers.

Although these statistics look bleak, children who have dealt with this kind of trauma can still grow into healthy adolescents in adults as long as the remaining parent can create an element of stability in the home. As mentioned above, this is never easy. But with the proper guidance and assistance the parent can provide the home life that children need.

One of the moments that still pains me the most when I think about what my children went through was when my oldest sat down next to me and said, "I must be stupid." I was immediately concerned by this statement coming from a child so young.

"Why?" I asked her.

"Because," she went on to respond, "I said nothing when daddy was telling me of his plans to leave." She went on to tell me that she "she just sat there and said nothing." I couldn't believe that a child of her age was

171

going through this in her mind, and that she just then felt the desire to speak up about it. She must have been carrying it around inside of her for such a long time. I reassured her that she most certainly was not stupid. I was furious. I could not believe that my husband felt that it was okay to put that kind of pressure, that kind of responsibility onto a seven-year-old. Seven years old should be concerned about play, about school work, about learning to read. They should not have to concern themselves with this. It was upsetting for me to picture him telling his daughter such things. He was so selfish, so careless. Eventually, although it took time and caring effort, I convinced her that it was not her fault. But I still have to wonder how long she sat there, alone, feeling that guilt.

I am certain that my children are experiencing a profound emptiness in their hearts for their father. The void that must be there. My son doesn't really know him, and still, he knows that something is missing. He calls him daddy. If you are in this rut, I strongly encourage you to seek help and to develop a support team who can minister to your children while you are recovering. It is not easy being in this situation because you are vulnerable, and so are your kids. It's difficult to help someone fully recover if you yourself have yet to recover. We must take care of ourselves before we are capable of caring for others. Fortunately, there are people to help bring you back to health and happiness.

⋅ Of course, to understand how to snap out of a state of diminished parenting and to provide distressed children with the support that they need, we must understand what is happening in the mind of the custodial parent who is suffering from this. It is similar to those who suffer from depression. They walk around in a fog of grief and exhaustion. From their vantage point, nothing is clear. They lack the ability to see the forest for the trees, meaning that they are so overwhelmed with grief that they lack the ability to parent properly. They are drained by their own emotions, so physically and emotionally exhausted that they cannot perform the daily tasks required. Basic household duties go undone, as does the essential task of fully caring for their children. For children to mature properly, they need constancy and structure, along with emotional stability and discipline. I knew I couldn't totally abandon my children, so I was doing the bare minimum. They had what they needed physically, but I was absent emotionally. I loved them, but I was in a thick haze.

So, what is the cause of diminished parenting? Why exactly does it happen? It happens because there is a mental breakdown in the custodial parent. It is due to the inability to cope with the transition that has taken place. The emotional pain that the person has is unbearable, and therefore she or he disconnects from the reality of it. They turn inward, away from outside stressors, and ultimately neglect their children because of it. The neglect is not intentional. It does not mean, in any way, that the custodial parent loves the children any less. It's simply a result of intense emotional trauma. Energy is completely depleted, because the person caring for the children now spends so much energy on thinking about all that transpired. There is no emotional energy left. A solid sense of time disappears, and the parent cannot put order to the day. All is exhaustion and chaos.

This mental exhaustion and hazy existence is exactly what happened to me. I went to work and barely functioned, only to return home and do just enough to keep the children alive. I washed them and fed them, and then would just go to my room. The world was too much to tolerate. I loved them, but the truth is, I was too exhausted even to leave my bed to pour juice for them. Sometimes they would bring the juice in just so I could fill their cups. This evolved into a habit of theirs. They knew I could not get out of bed, so they came to me. At no fault of their own, they ultimately developed habits that contributed to the overall disorder of my household. They were accustomed to going in and out of the refrigerator several times a day because I wasn't able to perform as a mother.

As I have mentioned before, their academic performance also suffered a great deal. They were not thriving in the classroom as they should have because

I simply could not help them with their schoolwork. I could not remind them to do it, could not make sure it was done neatly and correctly. Fortunately, my Godmother came over twice a week to help them with their homework. She especially helped my third grader, who was struggling in school. Because I lacked focus, I could not handle caring for two very young children and helping my oldest with her homework at the same time. She needed one on one care, and I simply could not provide that at the time. Now that the children are older, it has gotten easier. But then, I was stretched thin.

This is another instance in which a support team is absolutely vital. You have to have people in place that can help pick up the slack for times you fall short. Because during this time your energy is at an all time low, you're unable to focus on parenting.

There is no concrete timeframe for how long diminished parenting lasts. Like everything, it takes time. It also depends on the situation and the person. All scenarios are different. It depends on the parent because they control what happens in the household. Although there is no set time frame, and recovering will never be easy, I can say that the sooner the parent comes to the realization that they are asleep, the sooner they can change their behavior. I couldn't quite grasp how I was to recalibrate myself, and because I couldn't grasp this concept, I couldn't see. Because I couldn't see, I could not hear, and it affected my thought process. Everything was cloudy. None of my senses properly served me in the way that they needed to.

The thought process is critical to recovery because one must be able to think strategically in order to correct the breakdown in parenting that has occurred. In other words, you can't blank out. This is difficult because diminished parenting is a direct result of blanking out. It's a numbing of the mind in order to dull pain. You really don't want to think about the situation, so you can't fix the situation. You run away, hiding in your own mind, and try your best to ignore it. It's like sleeping with your eyes open.

For me to finally snap out of it, I needed someone to shake me. This person talked to me continuously about my parenting, to remind me of the jobs that I needed to do. This person taught me how to better relate to my children, how to run my household more efficiently. And this voice of reason didn't come until almost four years after my separation. So you can imagine the damage that occurred and how deep seeded the neglect was.

There is a societal perception that the father is the voice of rule in the household, and that if a father is not in the household, the children will become rebellious. But this isn't necessarily the case. If children have the proper guidance and structure, then they will thrive in a single parent household. The most important element to a child's success is a secure environment and a support system that helps to reinforce what you, the custodial parent, has established at home.

What Kids Need

I will focus a great deal on what children need in this book, because diminished parenting is a nearly inevitable side effect of trauma and depression. We need to know that we must do our best to reach out of our own sadness for the sake of our children. They need us, so we must know how best to care for them through our depression, and once it has ended. Caring for our children properly can help us heal, and it will help them heal as well. That is why the next few chapters will be dedicated to a discussion surrounding best parenting practices.

Kids have a lot of needs, and while some of these needs are simple, others are complex. It is up to us as parents to understand, and attempt to meet, our children's needs. When I was going through my separation, I was not meeting my children's' needs. I met them minimally, meaning I at least kept them fed. They were alive. They were not physically suffering to such an extent that any neglect was dangerous. But was not in any emotional state to take care of their emotional needs, and for children these needs are many. I was lucky that I had some support in my life, so my children had their needs better met when I was suffering.

Now, another important component to meeting your children's needs is making sure that your needs are also met. You cannot care for anyone until you care for yourself. Parenting is a selfless act but being too selfless will ultimately mean neglecting our children. I had neglected my own self, which is why my children were being neglected. I was physically and emotionally not healthy. It wasn't until I took care of myself that I could fully take care of children.

We all know, for the most part, our children's physical needs. They need food (ideally nutritious), shelter and a place to sleep that allows them to rest, medical care, and a healthy living environment. These physical needs are the building blocks upon which their other needs can go. If they are not well-rested, they cannot be happy. If they are not properly fed, they cannot focus, and they cannot thrive. They also need to be given proper medical care. This means we need to be aware about the general physical state that our children are in. It is up to us, as parents, to know when we should get our children to the doctor. They will not do this themselves. Now, the shelter that we provide our children needs to be more than shelter. It needs to be a safe and protected place in which they feel clean and comfortable. It cannot be a space that is so unclean that it makes them fall ill, or a place in which they experience abuse or neglect. Their physical needs also involve security. We also need to make sure that the food we feed them is not empty food, but rather healthy and nutritionally rich. If our children subsisted on a diet of Cheetos and ice cream all of the time, they would really suffer. It is up to the parent to make sure that the food our children eat is nutritionally sound, at least most of the time.

Now, it is time to talk about our children's emotional needs. First and foremost, children require unconditional love. For my children, this was disrupted when their father left. He was supposed to provide them with this, as their parent. But he did not.

I needed to make up for this. I needed to encourage them, to tell them that I would never leave them. That I would love them no matter what. That they are accepted by me unconditionally. I also needed to help them realize that God, the true Father, would never leave them. They are at the center of His world, as are all of His children.

Children also need the parent to help boost their confidence and self-esteem. This means praising them for a job well done, and nurturing in them a desire to learn and to explore. It means allowing them to take on new tasks, new responsibilities. Talk with them frequently, demonstrate interest in any and all activities in which they are participating.

When I went through my separation, I neglected my children as a result of diminished parenting. But I rose up from this, and rather than hurting my children, watching me struggle and overcome this struggle showed them that anything was possible. While this could have been a negative factor in my children's growth and development, I was able to transform it into something positive by demonstrating to them that nobody is immune to struggle. Nobody is immune to pain. They will experience heartache and suffering in their lives, but they will overcome this suffering. They are strong with and in God. I was not, at one point, meeting their needs. But I turned lack into a lesson, and in doing so I showed them that anything is possible.

This also goes with being honest. Honesty is important for children, and a crucial lesson to teach them. I was honest with my children and now, I hope, they can be honest with me. They know I am not perfect, and they are therefore unafraid of their own imperfections. This means that if they don't do well in school, rather than feeling ashamed about it, we can talk about how better to improve it the next time. We can have these honest conversations with one another.

Children need a lot of encouragement. They need encouragement to do their absolute best, but they also need encouragement to take risks. To try new things.

They need to be encouraged to play, to learn, to get dirty. They need to be encouraged to read, and to ask questions. Children's brains are always being formed, which means that they need encouragement along this process. With encouragement, they will be healthier and happier and will carry their positivity into adulthood.

While constructive criticism can benefit anyone, we need to be careful in how we approach this criticism with children. Never criticize the child directly, but rather criticize the behavior. Don't say something like, "you are a bad boy." This will cause the child to internalize the comment, and he will treat the words like a self-fulfilling prophecy. He will become a bad child. If you say, on the other hand, "this behavior was inappropriate because _____," then the child will respond more favorably. Children need to know why something is bad in order to avoid engaging in further poor behavior.

You should be your child's best teammate and cheerleader. We need to show trust in their ability to make good decisions, need to show trust in their character. We should not act argumentative towards them unnecessarily. This puts us on different teams, places us on different sides. We need to cheer for them when they do well and comfort them when they fail. We need to let them know that they will do better next time, that they have the potential to achieve incredible things.

We must have faith in our children and in their potential. Being a parent is scary. Sometimes we worry about them, but we must have faith that they will be okay, or else we will never let them try anything new. We must believe them when they talk to us about their goals and fears. If they think they can do it, then they can do it. Our job is to watch them try, sometimes to watch them struggle, and then to throw the rope towards them when they need it most. We must also have faith in ourselves, as parents. We must have faith in that what we are doing is right and that we can overcome our own challenges. If I did not eventually have faith that my God would lift me out of my dark place, then I would still be there. And my children would be suffering for it. I need to have faith that despite my own downfalls, that I can parent my children fully and successfully.

Speaking of faith, we need to encourage faith in God. If our children have faith in our Lord, then they will know that through Him all things are possible. They will know that He is always on their side, they always have a support system. The Bible says in Matthew 18:3, Verily I say unto you, except ye be converted, and become as little children, ye shall not enter into the Kingdom of Heaven. That is because faith comes naturally to them. It is up to us to nourish what is already there. Children have all of the traits that it takes to be a good believer. They are curious and loving. They have no problem at all believing what they cannot see, and their sense of wonder is incredible. We should all seek to emulate that. But we should also act as the spiritual authority in the home. Ask them questions about their faith and teach them the scriptures.

If you attend church, it is good to take your children with you. This way, they can ask questions that they might have. It allows them a space to learn and to grow. As I have mentioned, nurturing a strong community for children is truly essential towards building happy and healthy individuals. The church community can provide this. It can provide a stable background for children when parents fall short, as they inevitably will from time to time. My church fed my children when I could not do so.

Allow your children to ask questions about your faith. This will make them more engaged with it. If you don't know the answers, don't pretend that you do. You can offer to try and find the answers with your child, can ask a trusted authority at your church. This will improve your bond, teach your children to ask questions, and will make them think about faith on their own terms, to know God in a more intimate way.

When I was struggling, God helped to save me. For a very long time, I could not see the light on the other side of the Valley of the Shadow of Death. Once I made God my dwelling place, he helped me through it. Life will not always be easy. It was not easy for me and it will not be easy for my children. But if I raise them up with the Lord, with faith in them and faith in Him, then I know that they will make it through any struggle that they may face.

Kids don't need a lot of money or material things. They need a loving environment in which they can thrive. As parents, we face the challenge of feeling like we can never provide enough. Kids will always ask for new things, the newest shoes the newest games. Their friends have it, they might say to you. But we must remember that worldly pleasures are empty. Love is full. Our love provides feelings of fullness, as well as the love of God. If children have this, then they have everything. They do not need a new game or a television in their room. They need us to care for them in the best way possible. Spoiling our children is not the same as raising them. If we give our children all the nicest and newest items, they begin to confuse these material possessions with affection and will live their lives misguided. We can give our children love, and we can give our children experiences.

Being present in your children's lives

It is absolutely vital for parents to be present in their children's' lives. This is one of the most crucial steps towards successful child rearing, and one of the ways that you can reduce or reverse the negative effects of divorce or trauma on children. Being present for your children can be done in a variety of ways. When I was dealing with the trauma of my separation, I was there with my children, but I was not there for them. Which is exactly what present parenting should be.

Children need a secure place in which to return after a day at school or other place outside of the home. Especially if a child has undergone some sort of trauma, as is the case with divorce or another kind of loss, the child needs that stable base that he or she can learn to depend on. A strong parent-child bond is precisely what nurtures this kind of situation and environment. Children need to feel confident that they can talk to their custodial parent about what is happening in their lives. But this won't happen if a parent is disconnected. Sometimes, disconnection is inevitable. The custodial parent is dealing with their own trauma, feeling disconnected due to the impacts of depression. But this is where the parent, along with an ideally supportive community, can help to pull the parent out of the darkness and into healthier interactions with their children.

In order to be present in your child's life, it's a good idea to limit screen time. With the constant presence of electronics, being present is difficult for everybody. We can be anywhere and everywhere all at once. We can be on Facebook and chatting with our friends and reading the news, all pretty much at the same time. And children have access to these devices at younger and younger ages. They too are faced with constant distraction. Children eat while watching YouTube videos, or chat online when they should be communicating with you. While electronics won't go away, we can do our part as parents to limit their negative impact. While there are certainly benefits, too much of anything can be problematic. It's a good idea to limit both your screen time and theirs. Make sure that when you spend time together, it is distraction free.

The same way you want to reduce noise when you talk with God, you want to reduce outside noise when you talk to your children. By reducing outside noise, I don't mean shutting out sound. That will not happen if you are being active together. But I mean shutting out the noise of distraction that constant connection to electronics requires from us. Previously, I mentioned going to the laundromat with my children. I needed to pull my oldest away from her kindle in order to create this moment, but it was absolutely worth it. Had I let her stay glued to her screen, the moment would not have had the same magic. We never would have experienced that cohesion.

In a world swirling with distractions, it's also helpful to pay attention to where you are. There have been times when my children wanted to participate in an activity such as going to the park, and I felt like we didn't have time. I was too anxious about my schedule, about all that needed tending to. But what I really needed to tend to was my own health, and the health of my children. If you feel anxious because you are divided between spending time with your children and going to do the tasks you need to do for work or other projects, then it helps to take a step back, breathe, and remember that you are blessed to me in that moment.

Think about what you see, what you smell, what you hear. Think of your five senses in relation to the situation around you. You might be thinking about work, or about the loss that you faced, but what do you see when you watch your children? You might see them smiling. You probably hear them laughing. How does the sun on your face feel? Do you smell fresh air for the first time in a while? All of this will firmly plant you in the present moment with you children. It will allow you to enjoy your present while worrying more about the future later. With enough of this kind of time, you may begin to realize that your past loss and trauma is simply not as important as the beautiful present that surrounds you.

This increased connection is beyond beneficial for children. They feel respected and loved, and they feel safe. They are more likely to go to their parent if they face issues at school, which many children who have undergone trauma do. This relationship can last well into adolescence, when children face the most pressure. This increased connection is equally beneficial to a parent, especially for a parent who has undergone their own trauma. When I began to emerge from that valley, I was able to better connect with my children, and it turned it helped to speed up my own recovery.

While you are experiencing depression, or when you are dealing with the burden and incessant difficulties of single parenting, it's a good idea to remember that you are grateful. It may not feel like you have much, may feel like life itself is a burden, but if you do your best to remember the moments with your children that allow you to feel pure happiness, then gratitude for your life will follow. Sometimes, it helps to keep a gratitude diary. The Bible says in 1 Thessalonians 5:18, "In everything give thanks: for this is the will of God in Christ Jesus concerning you." Write down the moments and small joys that allow you to feel that happiness. While your life was not the way that it was, and it may be more difficult if you are on your own, remembering what you still have will benefit both you and your children. You will know that you have a reason to emerge on the other side of the Valley of the Shadow of Death, and they will know that they are loved. And this is the most important piece to good parenting: love.

Steps to creating order in your home

After I separated from my husband, my house fell into absolute disarray. It wasn't entirely my fault, because my circumstances did not allow me the same amount of time with which I could tend do household chores that I had before my separation. Also, I felt so depressed that there were days that I could not leave my bed. I barely noticed the mess, barely noticed the chaos, that was swirling constantly around me. Cleaning my house felt impossible. Dealing with my financial issues, my emotional state, and my household was too much. I focused only on what was absolutely necessary, which was keeping myself and my children alive.

In order to get myself back together, I needed to take small steps towards guaranteeing some level of presentation in my home. While it may seem like it is necessary to emerge from depression first in order to manage the home, creating an organized environment can actually help to reduce the impact of depression and to make you an overall more productive person. Gradually building up your old habits, such as making the bed every morning or mopping the floors once a week, can make you feel like you are again building up the habits that you once had. This is just one step, of many, to restoring normalcy in your life and in your home.

Of course, just because you know that it might make you feel better, in a moment in which you genuinely doubt that you will ever feel better, it can be hard to get up and take those first steps towards household order. It helps a great deal to create small, manageable lists. For example, you could focus on three things that you know need to get done. Maybe you need to clean the sink in the bathroom. Next time you go to the bathroom, make a point to clean the sink. Check it off your list. Do a load of laundry. Check it off your list. Simply visualizing your progress in the form of a checklist will do wonders for your feelings of productivity. You will start to feel like you're doing something, and soon those to-do lists will add up. Also, have the children pitch in and help. My daughters now basically wash the dishes. I barely have to.

Staying organized can also create feelings of control. After my separation, I felt like I had completely lost control of my personal and family life. And that's because in some ways, I had. I visualized a family life distinctly different from what I was experiencing. I wanted my children to live with both parents, I wanted to be married to my husband for life. Unfortunately, this is not always our reality. It takes time to acknowledge this new reality though, and to take control of it as it is. With an overall change in your internal environment your external environment will follow suite. With increased levels of organization, you may begin to think that if you can control the state of your house, then you can control other elements of your life. You can control certain emotions, certain reactions. Organization can be an empowering force in your life.

Avoiding clutter inevitably means throwing stuff away. This can be hard, because symbolically, after a separation, the partner who was abandoned is trying desperately to hold onto the past. In some ways, the abandoned spouse may feel like they are preserving the way that things were. Items in the house go untouched because maybe, just maybe they think, the spouse who left will return and if the house is how it once was, then everything else will be how it once was. This isn't the case. We need to throw things away. Or on the other hand you desire something new and fresh to erase the heartache that you have experienced.

We especially need to throw things away if we are undergoing a divorce. If it was something you had as a couple and no longer use, you should toss it. Even if it wasn't something that has to do with your ex-husband or ex-wife, you should still throw it away or donate it if it is no longer in use. This will make you realize that you are shedding the old you, reshaping yourself and your home in a new image. Your life has now changed. There is no point in dwelling on the past and holding on to these old items will allow you to realize that your relationship is over. But even though it is over, and even though you are feeling pain, you can still throw away the old and emerge with the new. Sometimes, cleansing your home of unused belongings can feel like you are purging the past. It can, in many ways, be therapeutic.

One way to organize your home and to create an increased connection with your kids is to do chores together. Kids bristle at the idea of this, but after a while they may start to value it as a time in which we can all spend time together. Additionally, it teaches them responsibility and allows them to grow into employable and reliable adults. It's like Proverbs 22:6 states, "train up a child in the way he should go, even when he is old, he will not depart from it."

You can designate one day in which you all clean. You could listen to music together, taking turns choosing the artist or radio station. The younger children can be responsible for easier tasks, but they will inevitably feel important by having these tasks designated to them. Make them feel like what they're doing is vital for the appearance of their own house, and they will learn the pride of a job well-done. The oldest children can take on more responsibility and will also feel like they are more adult for it. It makes your housekeeping more manageable for you and has benefits for the children as well.

Keeping your house clean is not about making your home spotless all of the time. It is more about making sure that it is warm and welcoming, that it is a space in which you and your children can feel comfortable. According to 1 Corinthians 14:33, God is not a God of disorder, but of peace. We must reflect God in everything we do, which means maintaining a peaceful and orderly household. He did not say that our house has to be spotless, but we must try and strive for peace.

Creating a nurturing environment

Children who have experienced trauma need an especially nurturing environment. And this does not only mean nurturing in the sense that they are clothed and fed. I was doing this for my children. I made sure that they had what they needed physically. But this is not enough. We must also nurture our children spiritually. It means more than making the house in which they spend some time and sleep. It means creating a refuge in the home, with you as the parent their companion and protector. This means that you must make your home warm and caring, a place children want to return to. Their physical selves must certainly be cared for, but their emotional and spiritual needs must also be cared for.

Human beings are, very often, a product of their environment. We can go back to the garden example that I mentioned earlier. Children are like flowers, they are the healthy garden plants that are beautiful and designed to thrive. But if we do not tend to the garden, and if weeds are allowed to take over, then our plants will not experience the garden as they should: a place to grow and to reach ever higher, a place in which they feel peace and are allowed to grow to their full potential.

Now, let's talk about the home as a garden. The plants (children) need care. They need water, sure, but they also need sunlight. This sunlight is love, it is the spiritual and emotional care that must be present in order to create a truly nurturing environment. The water feeds their physical needs, but without the sunlight, they will not grow.

While the home needs to be a nurturing center, there should also be a nurturing center within the home. This can be the living room, or a kitchen table. Basically, it just needs to be the center of some activity. It can be a place that kids go to do homework, where everyone gathers to eat. But the entire point of it is that it needs to be welcoming to an extent that people want to be there. This can be a place both of ritual and spontaneity. It can be a place where people go every night to eat in one moment, and then it can be an impromptu painting station the next. While gathering together to watch a movie or a TV show can be great, it shouldn't be the primary gathering place. This prevents healthy and meaningful interaction, leaving the time spent together empty.

In addition to creating a nurturing environment outside of the home, it is also important to create a nurturing environment outside of it. This means that we should focus on making ourselves part of strong communities and strong community groups. One of my problems, after my separation, was that I had not built a strong support system. I had always looked inward, rather than outward. I looked at my direct family unit as my priority, not realizing that I could have been benefiting them by creating more extended support systems.

Community takes a number of different forms. It can be strong ties with extended family. It can be a local library, with parents and the children taking advantage of the provided programs and activities. For me, it was my church. My church community has been vital in providing me with the support I needed through my separation. Single parenting is hard, so we need to depend on other people to help raise our children into strong and stable adults. It takes a village to raise a child. It may sound cliché, but it's true.

When I was unable to feed my children, the church provided. When I was unable to help my daughter with her homework, my Godmother helped me. We need these networks, need people to help us nurture our children both physically and emotionally during those times when we are unable to do so ourselves. When children are small, their environment is relegated primarily to the home. As they grow older, especially in adolescence, their environment is within their surrounding community. The home can still play a central role, but then they will be spending time with friends. They will be playing sports or playing instruments or, basically, developing interests away from their home life. This can still be a nurturing environment, but especially if they were provided with such environments in their earlier years.

Eating, and cooking, with your children

People often say that the most important thing you can do with, and for, your child is simply to eat with them. When I was suffering through my depression, I could scarcely get out of bed. My children brought me juice to pour them. They didn't have stable meals, but rather got food out of the refrigerator as they saw fit. I did not do this because I wanted to be neglectful, or because I don't value my children's health, but rather because the state that I was in prevented me from seeing what was right in front of me. I simply couldn't see beyond my emotions. While eating with your children sounds simple, this doesn't necessarily mean that it's always easy. In my case, I was suffering from extreme depression, and getting up to do anything was draining. I needed help to get out of that state. A lot of help. For other people, it may be that their schedule is totally demanding. But if we get to the point where we can, we should make eating with our children a priority.

Researchers have found that when children sit down at the dinner table and talk with their parents, their vocabulary is boosted a great deal. This, in turn, boosts their future reading ability. Studies have shown that a regular mealtime is a more powerful indicator of high scores than time spent in school, time spent participating in extracurriculars, or time spent doing homework. In addition to improved academic performance, regular meals with a parent mean that children tend to eat healthier. Obviously, if a child is in charge of feeding him or herself, then that child will not make the most nutritionally sound choices. It would be ice cream and french fries for dinner every single night.

Children that eat dinner with a parent are less likely to engage in risky behavior as an adult. They are also less likely to suffer from depression. If a child is bullied, he or she is more likely to find an outlet eating dinner with the parent and will not suffer the negative impacts of that bullying quite as drastically. The same can be said for the parent involved - if the parent is interacting regularly with her children, it can help to ease anxiety. Even in high-stress situations.

While I know that eating a meal together is not a complete answer, I do know that it can help heal both a parent and children who have been through a traumatic event. It increases the bond and makes it known amongst all involved that there is a positive group structure, some solidity, in the home. I also know that some families simply might not be able to make mealtime together a regular occurrence. Some parents work in the evenings. But taking the time to talk to your children during any meal, even if only briefly during breakfast, can still have a positive impact. In our busy worlds, with everyone rushing around to various activities and with parents working long hours, a meal time might be the only time we have to really connect. And that connection is important for families healing from a painful experience.

In my household, this was especially important. When someone who is supposed to be a reliable figure leaves, such as the father and the husband, the children will inevitably crave signs of stability. Sometimes, despite financial hardship and emotions, a meal together can be a good way to create that. I could not create that at first. I was too depressed. But I realized that it was a good way to show my children that we were still a family, even if their father did not want to be there anymore.

Of course, just eating as a family is not necessarily enough to create solid relationships. Eating with your children should be about interacting with them, about allowing them the space to talk about their days. You could cook a twelve-course meal and your kids would not benefit in the same way they would if you just asked them how their day was. It's a time for everyone to talk about the good and the bad parts to the day.

Now, in addition to eating with your kids you can go one step further and cook with them. This is beneficial for all children in all types of families, but it is especially beneficial for those who have been through a traumatic situation. It is therapeutic for both the children and for the parent. It doesn't necessarily matter what you cook together. It can be something simple, or it can be something more complicated as the kids grow. If children feel that they are contributing something to the household, then their self-esteem will rise. This is important for children of divorce, because occasionally, their self-esteem suffers. It also allows the child the time to talk. And if they need to talk about a difficult subject, they can do so while staying busy in the kitchen, which helps to relieve some of the tension.

There are a number of benefits to teaching children how to cook while they are young. For one, cooking is a necessary skill that leads to self-sufficiency. Many adults don't know how to cook because they were never taught while they were at home. So, they rely on fast food or carry out, which is far less healthy than a home cooked meal. But in addition to being a necessary life skill, cooking also offers children the chance to improve in other areas as well. Learning how to cook improves a child's ability to read critically and to do math. Many recipes require the cook to double, or halve, the recipe. This means children will need to do some mental math to make sure that they are cooking correctly. They will also learn to read the recipe very carefully. And, of course, what is cooking besides one big real life science experiment?

While I would love to provide a meal for my children all of the time, the reality is that I can't always be there to meet their needs at all times of the day. If I can cook with my children, then as they grow up I can more adequately trust their snacking decisions. If they know how to make a healthy snack, I know they won't be reaching for unhealthy foods after school. It also then gives them a sense of independence. This will make them proud, knowing that they can take care of themselves if they need to.

The confidence boost that comes from learning how to cook is indispensable. If a child can learn to make a meal, the child will feel like he or she can learn to make other things or do other activities as well. It also makes them want to try new foods, and therefore they will be more willing to branch out in real life. It also gives you a chance to talk to your child about what he or she should be eating, which will serve them well when they are on their own.

This is also beneficial for the parent. It teaches a parent patience, reminding us that it is not always how fast something gets done (try cooking with three kids and tell me it will be fast) but who you're getting it done with. It forces you to slow down when you think that your life won't normally let you. And, as everything with your children, it reminds you of all that you have to be grateful for. I have food to cook, you can think. And I have someone who wants to cook with me.

Watching tv

The television has now become a sort of family centerpiece. It is where the family most often gathers. Or, in more and more households, everyone watches something different on their various devices, meaning that everyone is watching television at the same time, but nobody is watching anything together. I do not think that television, even when viewed together, should be a cornerstone of family life, but I do think that it can occasionally offer benefits if the family all gathers around one televisions show or movie. Now, I know that not everyone will always have the same taste, and that sometimes you will need to sit and watch a show separately to decompress. This is also okay. We are not perfect. But I am encouraging people to spend time away from the television more often, and when the craving to watch TV strikes, to find something that you can all watch together. At least once in a while.

Kids now have so much access to screen and televisions. Gathering around one program to watch together does not always make sense, nor could we, as parents, control all of that anyway. We can't be home all of the time, and if our children have their own devices, which they inevitably will, then we just need to do our best to control what we can control. If we try our best to completely limit our children's time in front of the TV, computer, tablet, kindle, etc. we are stretching ourselves truly thin. Additionally, it's then possible that our children will simply decide to hide their activity from us. Which makes us less involved when the goal is always to be more involved.

Now, not all television or screen time is the same. For example, a well-made educational program can have a lot of benefits for younger children. Especially in those moments when we cannot always be there for their education. It will never take place of parental involvement, and probably should not be excessive, but a little bit of interactive and informative programming can actually benefit young kids. Kids can learn colors, language, and even some reading in this way.

Now, when your kids are really young, it's a lot easier to monitor what they are viewing. You're basically focused on making sure that what they watch is at least a little educational, and that they aren't watching too much television. But once your kids get older, it's important to make sure that they aren't watching anything that is too violent or sexually explicit. And this can be hard. With social media, and the increasingly easy access of online videos, it is very difficult to monitor what our kids are watching in their own time. The best thing to do in this case is probably to set positive viewing examples when you watch TV together, and to make sure that your kids can talk to you about what they see online. Let them know what is appropriate and set all of the limits that you can.

We need to make sure that our children are not replacing television with other, healthier activities. For example, playing outside. If the weather is nice, your children should almost certainly be outside rather than inside in front of a screen. Sometimes this means you need to take everyone out and go on a walk or go to the park. Now remember what I said about vitamin D - Vitamin D deficiency can have a huge impact on your mental health. This is why going outside is so important for children and adults of all ages. Your children need the sun and the exercise, and you do too. This is especially beneficial to parents who are depressed and feeling anxiety. Even a little time in the sun can boost mood. When I was depressed, I never wanted to leave the house. I didn't realize that this was making my depression worse.

It's easy for children and parents who have experienced trauma to want to mindlessly zone out to television. We don't have to think, and we can sit back and escape from our lives by watching other people's. This very often does more harm than good, however. It makes it so that we can't acknowledge what in our lives is making us suffer. We never have to deal with our problems. And more problems down the line could easily crop up. Childhood obesity is at a high, and too much television contributes to this. It also creates distance between family members. Time meant socializing is more important for a child's development than screen time will ever be.

Of course, there are some moments in which watching television together can be a fun and healthy activity. For example, if there is a movie that the entire family is interested in seeing, you can make this an exciting event. Maybe you can pop some popcorn, and all sit together to watch the screen. Family movie nights have been a favored past time for years. Of course, it's best to then talk about the movie together afterwards. What did you like about it? What didn't you like about it? Who was your favorite character? Why? This can lead to some very stimulating interaction between children and their parent or parents. It teaches children how to have a conversation and how to think critically.

I have three children of different ages, so finding a movie or television show that is age appropriate for everyone is not always easy. But usually, there is something that will appeal to all involved. I need to make sure I ask for everyone's opinions before choosing. If we can't all agree on something, then we can take turns deciding. And usually, the kids enjoy the experience of being together and enjoying something more than the movie itself anyways.

I mention television because watching television is actually linked to too much depression. Adults and children alike tend to watch more TV when they're depressed, but watching more television also increases levels of depression. This is partially because, when we use television in an attempt to make our bad feelings go away, then we are enforcing the habit that we don't actually need to solve our problems. We look for a temporary fix.

Ultimately, we use television as a substitute. If we can't interact with our kids, we use the television as a babysitter, as a sort of parental substitute. Or, both our children and us are using the television to substitute as a real solution. We know that the only solution is God, only he can get us through the Valley of the Shadow of Death, but in that moment, the television feels like it is lifting us away. But it only lasts the length of the television program. Then it's gone. We are back to our lives and to the fake solutions we have created. Television is a distraction from the real solution that is God. Television has almost turned into the false God that we were once warned about.

I am not saying that television is evil, but I am saying that it should not be treated like a God. And if we do, it will turn into something truly problematic. We need to use it as a means of interacting with each other very occasionally, not as a substitute for other human interaction or physical activity. Especially in a household that has dealt with trauma. It is then especially important that we interact in healthy ways and use the television sparingly, that way we can better emerge from our darkness.

<u>Parenting according to the Bible</u>

There are so many parenting books present in the world today. There are so many parenting styles, so much advice to parents on how best to take care of their children. The truth is though, the Bible is the best parenting book. If we parent as God wants us to, then our children will thrive. God tells our children that they must obey us, but he also encourages us to balance heart to heart, nurturing parenting with admonition. If we are purely disciplinarians, then our children will well with anger and rebellion. Ephesians 6:4 says, "Fathers, do not provoke your children to anger, but bring them up in the discipline and instruction of the Lord."

We must request that our children honor and respect us, but they also need to be nurtured by us. They need to feel like they can come to us with their day to day concerns. We also must lead by example. If we live a full and virtuous life, our children will likely do the same. They will make mistakes just as we make mistakes, for nobody is perfect. But if they turn to the Lord as we turn to the Lord in times of darkness, then they will be whole.

Children need rules, otherwise an order-less household could ensue. This is not beneficial to anyone. It does not help the parent, and it does not help the children. A parent may find themselves throwing their hands up in exasperation, while as the children will lack guidance and discipline. This will make them unruly in school, and they will likely act out. The child will feel that he or she makes their own rules, and we all know that those rules would lack proper boundaries. Even the best child does not have the experience necessary to set appropriate boundaries. It would be absolute chaos. In the old testament, God gave Moses the ten commandments in order to guide his children through some sense of rule. We still adhere to those today. These are our parental guidelines.

Now, this doesn't mean that the child should exclusively be disciplined all of the time. Children need room to explore, to make mistakes. This is how they grow. If children cannot make their own mistakes, they will never mature. If a parent tries too hard to parent using fear and the rule of absolute law, then this will inevitably produce negative results. Children will either try and hide bad behavior because they fear the consequences, or they will rebel later on. They may lose control once they have freedom after they leave home, creating more chaos as a result of too many rules and too much punishment when they were at home. According to James 1:19-20, "the anger of man does not produce the righteousness of God."

While discipline is sometimes necessary, it alone will not allow our children to thrive. We must explain to them why their actions were wrong. Why they were hurtful. If we simply tell them what they are expected to do and how to behave, rather than why, then our orders will only go so far. They will feel meaningless. They need to know not only the consequences for disobeying, but the benefits of obedience. You need to demonstrate that your rules were made out of love. Then they will be more likely to follow your lead. They will mature fully and beautifully.

Children will never learn rules overnight. This is a constant process by which we, as the parents, need to oversee. Our children will make mistakes and we need to understand this, need to make peace with that idea. When I was going through my separation, I did not have the energy to see that my children were living undisciplined lives. My oldest daughter struggled with her homework, and I could neither remind her to finish it nor help her to get it done. This is where our community comes in. My Godmother played a vital role in making sure that my daughter had the instruction that we needed. We are not meant to be alone. We are one body in Christ, and we must act in that way.

Getting angry at our children too often will not nurture a love of God within them, which should be our ultimate goal as parents. The home should encourage the desire of the Lord, not the desire of the parent or the children. This will strike the balance we are looking for, that balance between discipline and nurturing care. While God gave us ten commandments, all of them can be reduced to the most important tenet, "love God and love others." Basically, treat others as you want to be treated and respect one another. This is the single most important component that we can stress when we teach our children how to live. If we teach them how to love, then they will know no boundaries.

About the Author

T.L. Best resides in Queens, New York. She works for the Unified Court System and is the mother of three children. T.L. Best has taught biblical studies for over twenty years and has a bachelor's degree in Religious Education from the Mason Kelly Washington Religious Training Institute. She is currently a member of Christ Tabernacle Christian Fellowship where she serves as an on-staff counselor. She is the founder of Make Me Your Dwelling Place Ministries.

Made in United States
Orlando, FL
06 September 2022